D0538051
THE SAGA OF
DARREN SHAN
TRIALS OF DEATH
VOLUME
5
Story: Darren Shan
Manga: Takahiro Arai

A SUMMARY OF VAMPIRE MOUNTAIN:

DARREN—ACCOMPANIED BY HIS MASTER, MR. CREPSLEY, AND THE LITTLE PERSON, HARKAT—HAS TRAVELED TO VAMPIRE MOUNTAIN, THE HEART OF THE VAMPIRE WORLD, TO ATTEND THE VAMPIRE COUNCIL, AN EVENT THAT ONLY OCCURS ONCE EVERY TWELVE YEARS. HOWEVER, THE VAMPIRE PRINCES ARE DISPLEASED WITH MR. CREPSLEY FOR BREAKING THEIR RULES AND TURNING A CHILD INTO A HALF-VAMPIRE. DARREN MUST STEEL HIMSELF FOR THE TERRIBLE TRIALS OF INITIATION TO DISPEL HIS MASTER'S SHAME AND PROVE THAT HE IS WORTHY OF BEING A VAMPIRE.

TRIALS OF DEATH

CONTENTS

EIGHT YEARS AGO, MR. CREPSLEY TURNED ME INTO A HALF-VAMPIRE. BUT I WAS STILL A CHILD, AND THAT GOES AGAINST VAMPIRE LAW.

IN ORDER TO REGAIN HIS HONOUR ...
...AND PROVE MY OWN STRENGTH ...

...I HAVE CHOSEN TO UNDERTAKE THE TRIALS OF INITIATION.
GYU (SQUEEZE)

BUT OF THE TRUE TERROR OF THE TRIALS, AND THE CRUEL FATE THAT AWAITED ME AT THE END OF THEM...

...I WAS WOEFULLY IGNORANT.

CHAPTER 35: A VAMPIRE COUPLE

CHAPTER 35:
A VAMPIRE COUPLE

IF YOU SHOULD FAIL THE TRIALS, THERE IS ONLY ONE OUTCOME.
YOU WILL BE TAKEN TO THE HALL OF DEATH...
...AND DROPPED ONTO THE STAKES UNTIL YOU ARE DEAD!!

IF I FAIL THE TRIALS OF INITIATION ...
...I WILL BE EXE-CUTED.

I SHOULD HAVE EXPLAINED BETTER ...
...BUT IT'S TOO LATE TO TAKE ANY OF IT BACK NOW.
I'M SORRY, DARREN. IF ONLY I'D KNOWN IT WOULD LEAD TO THIS...
WHY ARE YOU APOLOGIZING, KURDA?
TRUE, IT WAS MORE THAN A BIT OF A SHOCK WHEN I FOUND OUT.
BUT EVEN IF I'D KNOWN THE RISKS, I THINK I WOULD HAVE ACCEPTED.
I WOULD'VE HAD TO!
FOR MR CREPSLEY'S SAKE ...
...AND FOR MY OWN.
DARREN...
NO, THE TRIALS ARE ONLY THE FIRST TEST FOR WOULD-BE GENERALS.
THERE ARE OTHER TESTS OF STRENGTH, ENDURANCE, AND WISDOM, WHICH COME LATER.
SO, GAVNER ...
...WILL I BE ALLOWED TO BECOME A VAMPIRE GENERAL IF I PASS THE TRIALS?

BY PASSING THE TRIALS OF INITIA-TION...
...YOU PROVE THAT YOU ARE A HARDY INDIVIDUAL, WORTHY OF BEING A VAMPIRE.
IT IS NECESSARY IF YOU WANT TO BE SEEN AS A VAMPIRE OF GOOD STANDING AND BE GIVEN RESPECT BY YOUR FELLOWS.
BUT MANY VAMPIRES UNDERTAKE THE TRIALS, EVEN IF THEY'RE NOT KEEN ON BEING GENERALS.
AND HOW MANY TESTS ARE THERE, AGAIN?
FIVE.
THE ORDER IS DETER-MINED AT RANDOM.
THE TRIALS TAKE PLACE ONE NIGHT AFTER ANOTHER.
A DAY'S REST IS ALL YOU'RE ALLOWED IN BE-TWEEN.
SO YOU HAVE TO BE ESPECIALLY CAREFUL AT THE START.
IF YOU GET INJURED EARLY ON, YOU WON'T HAVE MUCH TIME TO RECOVER.
ACTUALLY...
...DARREN MIGHT GET LUCKY THERE.
THE FESTIVAL OF THE UNDEAD IS ALMOST UPON US!
GATA (THUD)
OH? WHAT'S THAT?

WE CELEBRATE WITH A HUGE FEAST WHEN EVERY VAMPIRE WHO'S COMING TO COUNCIL HAS ARRIVED!
WHEN THE LAST ARRIVES, THE FESTIVAL BEGINS, AND NO OFFICIAL BUSINESS MAY TAKE PLACE FOR THREE NIGHTS AND DAYS!
THE STONE OF BLOOD SAYS THAT THERE ARE ONLY THREE STILL ON THEIR WAY.
THAT'S RIGHT! IF THE FESTIVAL STARTS DURING YOUR TRIALS, YOU'LL HAVE A THREE-NIGHT BREAK.
THAT WOULD BE A GREAT BONUS!
BUT ONLY ...
...IF THE LATE-COMERS ARRIVE IN TIME.
WHY ARE YOU SO SURE I'LL FAIL?
WE WON'T KNOW UNTIL I TRY IT.
IT'S NOT THAT I THINK POORLY OF YOU.
YOU'RE JUST TOO YOUNG AND INEXPERIENCED FOR THE TRIALS.
THEY HAVE ASKED TOO MUCH OF YOU. IT JUST ISN'T FAIR...
ZA (ZSHH)
STILL WHINING ABOUT FAIRNESS, KURDA?

ZA
ZA (ZSHH)
IT COULD BE THE DEATH OF YOUR OWN PUPIL.
YOU WERE VERY QUICK TO AGREE TO THE TRIALS, LARTEN.
THE ONLY REASON THAT I BROUGHT DARREN HERE TO THE COUNCIL AT ALL...
... WAS TO CONFESS TO MY MISTAKE.
IF I HAD THE CHOICE, I WOULD FACE THE CHALLENGE, TO CLEAR MY OWN NAME.
BUT THE PRINCES ELECTED DARREN.
I AM CONFIDENT THAT HE HAS WHAT IS NECESSARY TO PASS THE TRIALS.
ALL IS FAR FROM LOST.
THE PRINCES HAVE AGREED TO ALLOW DARREN THE USE OF AN OLD CLAUSE.

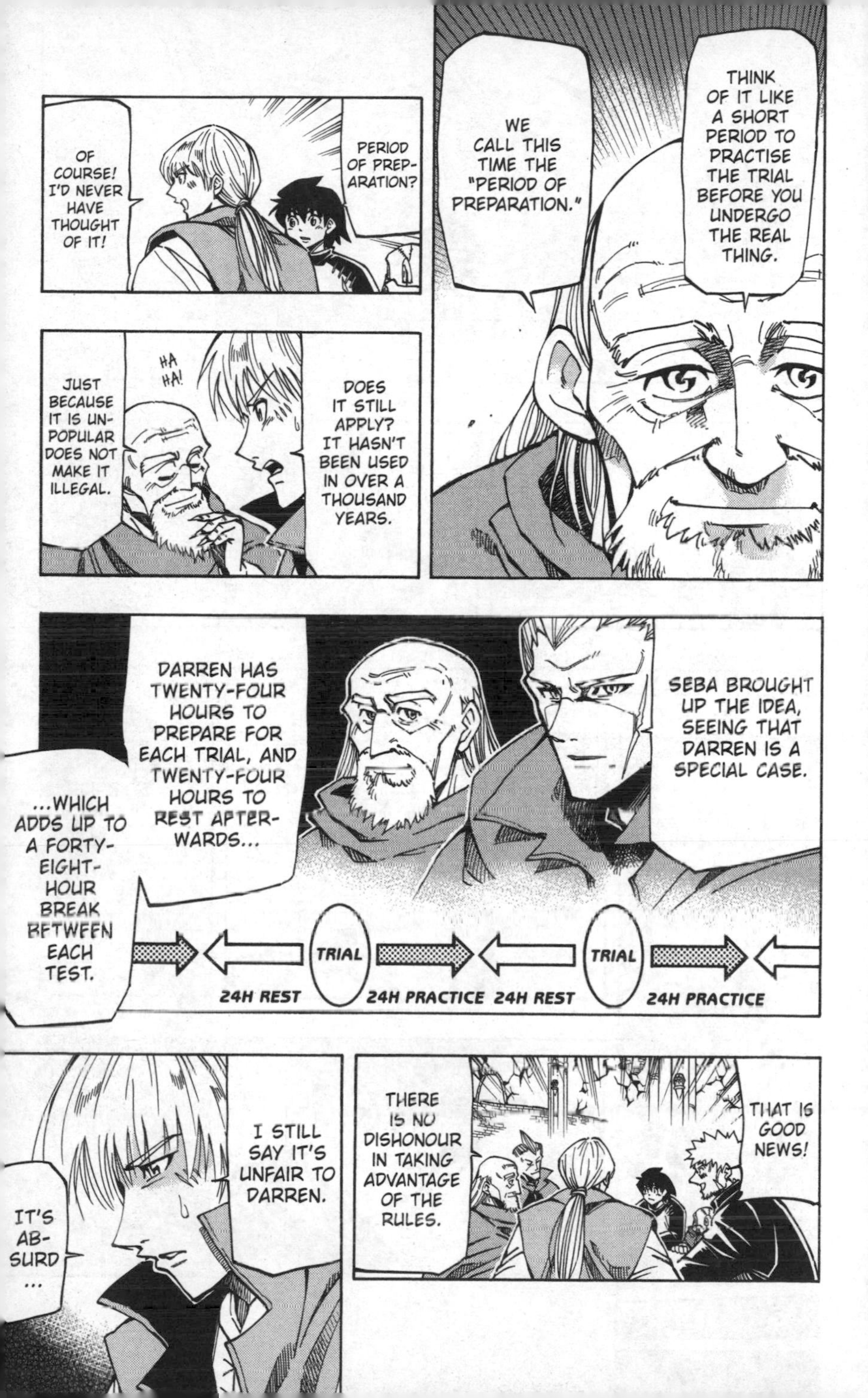
THINK OF IT LIKE A SHORT PERIOD TO PRACTISE THE TRIAL BEFORE YOU UNDERGO THE REAL THING.
WE CALL THIS TIME THE "PERIOD OF PREPARATION."
PERIOD OF PREP-ARATION?
OF COURSE! I'D NEVER HAVE THOUGHT OF IT!
DOES IT STILL APPLY? IT HASN'T BEEN USED IN OVER A THOUSAND YEARS.
HA HA!
JUST BECAUSE IT IS UN-POPULAR DOES NOT MAKE IT ILLEGAL.
SEBA BROUGHT UP THE IDEA, SEEING THAT DARREN IS A SPECIAL CASE.
DARREN HAS TWENTY-FOUR HOURS TO PREPARE FOR EACH TRIAL, AND TWENTY-FOUR HOURS TO REST AFTER-WARDS...
...WHICH ADDS UP TO A FORTY-EIGHT-HOUR BREAK BETWEEN EACH TEST.
TRIAL
TRIAL
24H PRACTICE
24H REST
24H PRACTICE
24H REST
THAT IS GOOD NEWS!
THERE IS NO DISHONOUR IN TAKING ADVANTAGE OF THE RULES.
I STILL SAY IT'S UNFAIR TO DARREN.
IT'S AB-SURD...

SHIIIN
(SILENCE)

I WILL SEE YOU IN THE HALL OF PRINCES TOMORROW, DARREN.
REST IS VITAL.
GATA
(THUMP)
OKAY...
TOMORROW!
REST WELL.
SEE YOU.

TOBO
(TRUDGE)
TOBO
YOU WILL BE... FINE, DARREN.
I THINK THAT... ONCE YOU START... YOU'LL FIND THAT...
...IT'S NOT... SO HARD.
......
YEAH. THAT'S THE SPIRIT.
THANKS, HARKAT...

I DIDN'T GET A FULL DAY'S SLEEP ...
ARRA!
GU (GRAB)
HOW ARE YOU?
YOU LOOK TIRED.
I HOPE YOU'RE NOT TOO UPSET...
... ABOUT WHAT I SAID IN THE HALL OF PRINCES.
I DON'T BELIEVE IN GOING EASY ON VAMPIRES, EVEN IF THEY'RE CHILDREN.
OURS IS A HARD LIFE, NOT SUITED TO THE WEAK.

AS I SAID, I THINK YOU'LL PASS THE TRIALS...
...BUT IF YOU DON'T, I WON'T STEP IN TO PLEAD FOR YOUR LIFE.
I UNDER-STAND.
WE'RE STILL FRIENDS ?
OF COURSE!
IF YOU NEED HELP PREPARING, CALL ON ME.
I HAVE BEEN THROUGH THE TRIALS THREE TIMES.
THREE TIMES !?
TO PROVE TO MYSELF MORE THAN ANYONE ELSE THAT I AM A WORTHY VAMPIRE.
THAT IS A VERY KIND OFFER, ARRA.
WE WILL MOST CER-TAINLY BEAR IT IN MIND.
WELL, LOOK AT YOU.
COURTE-OUS AS EVER, LARTEN.
AND AS HANDSOME TOO.
!?
HA HA...

AND YOU ARE AS BEAUTIFUL AS EVER.
......
I KNOW.

PAKU (GAPE)
PAKU
UTTORI (GAZE)

UHH...
I SEE.
IS SHE...
...AN OLD GIRL-FRIEND?
IF YOU MUST KNOW...
...ARRA WAS ONCE...
...MY MATE.
OHON (AHEM)
WHAT ARE YOU GRINNING ABOUT?
NEE-HEE!
NOTHING...

HUH?
YOU MEAN SHE WAS YOUR WIFE?
IN A MANNER OF SPEAKING.
YOU NEVER TOLD ME YOU WERE MARRIED!
I AM NOT— ANY-MORE— BUT I USED TO BE.
WHAT HAPPENED? DID YOU GET A DIVORCE?
GEHO (KOFF)
GOHON (AHEM)
VAMPIRES NEITHER MARRY NOR DIVORCE AS HUMANS DO.
WE MAKE TEMPORARY MATING COMMIT-MENTS INSTEAD.
WHAT DO YOU MEAN?
VAMPIRES MAY CHOOSE TO MATE FOR A TIME, BUT THEY MAY FREELY PART WAYS WHENEVER THEY WISH.
PORI (SCRATCH)
PORI
SINCE WE CANNOT HAVE CHILDREN AS HUMANS DO...
...VERY FEW VAMPIRES CHOOSE TO SPEND THEIR VERY LONG LIVES WITH ONE MATE.
VAMPIRES CAN'T HAVE CHILDREN?
AS YOU HAVE MOST LIKELY NOTICED, IT IS ONE OF THE REASONS THERE ARE SO FEW FEMALE VAMPIRES.
BUT NOT THE ONLY ONE.

DO YOU STILL HAVE FEELINGS FOR ARRA?
I ADMIRE AND RESPECT HER.
I SEE...
SHIUUUU (HSSSSS)
KAAAA (BLUSH)
DO YOU LOVE HER?
THAT'S NOT WHAT I MEAN.
FUN (BAH)
FUN
IT IS TIME TO PRESENT OUR-SELVES TO THE PRINCES! NO DALLY-ING!
HEY!
OH, LOOK!
DA!! (LEAP)
THEY MAKE A GOOD COUPLE.
...RIGHT BEFORE RISKING MY LIFE FOR A TRIAL.
THAT'S A KINDA FUNNY THING TO LEARN...

DARREN SHAN, TO THE FRONT!
YES, SIRE!

ARE YOU PREPARED TO ACCEPT ANY TRIAL?
YES, SIRE!
SU (SHH)
ARE YOU PREPARED TO CHALLENGE CLEANLY, FOR THE HONOUR OF YOUR MASTER?
YES, SIRE!

VERY WELL.
WE SHALL DRAW THE FIRST TRIAL.

UP HERE.
KA (TOKK)
YES, SIR!

GARA (CLUNK)
GASHA (CLANK)
YOU WILL SELECT A SINGLE STONE.
THE FIRST TRIAL...
IF I FAIL... I WILL DIE.
I PUT ON A BRAVE FACE...
I HAD TO ACCEPT!
FOR MY OWN SAKE.
DARREN...
...BUT I'M STILL SCARED STIFF INSIDE!
GO ON. TAKE YOUR STONE.
......
GOKU... (GULP)
GASHA (CLUNK)
GARA (CLACK)
NUMBER ELEVEN!
THE FIRST TRIAL SHALL BE...
11

...THE AQUATIC MAZE !!!
YOU WILL REPORT FOR THE FIRST TRIAL TOMORROW AT DUSK, TWENTY-FOUR HOURS FROM NOW.
USE YOUR PERIOD OF PREPARATION WISELY.
I WILL.
AQUATIC MAZE? WHAT COULD IT BE?
IS THAT GOOD OR BAD?
YOU'RE NOT GOING TO TELL ME YOU CAN'T SWIM, DARREN!
TA (TEK)
OH!
VANEZ!!
YO!

I WENT AND SPOKE TO THE PRINCES.
THEY WON'T OBJECT IF YOU ASK ME TO BE YOUR TRIALS TUTOR.
REALLY!?
SHOW HIM YOUR GRATITUDE, DARREN.
VANEZ KNOWS THE TRIALS INSIDE AND OUT.
OH, STOP IT...
THANK YOU, VANEZ.
DON'T EVEN BOTHER THANKING ME. IT'S NOTHING!
SO MANY PEOPLE ARE OFFERING THEIR HELP OUT OF CONCERN FOR ME...
MY VAMPIRE COMPANIONS...
...FOR EIGHT YEARS, THEY'VE BEEN WITH ME.
GYU (SQUEEZE)
I'VE NEVER BEEN ALONE!

EVEN A FULLY-GROWN VAMPIRE PREPARES CAREFULLY FOR THE TRIALS.
BAKI (CRIK)
BOKI (CRAKK)
I DON'T KNOW HOW MUCH WE'LL ACCOMPLISH IN TWENTY-FOUR HOURS ...
...BUT IT'LL BE ROUGH.
YOUR LIFE DEPENDS ON KEEPING UP!
THAT'S JUST WHAT I'M HOPING FOR!
ZA (ZSHH)
THE FIRST TRIAL IS THE AQUATIC MAZE!!
LET'S GET TRAIN-ING!!!

THIS IS IMPOSSIBLE!
HOW CAN I BE EXPECTED TO PULL THIS OFF JUST TEN HOURS FROM NOW!?
DON'T PANIC, DARREN!
BASHAA (SPLASH)
YOUR GREATEST FOE IN THIS TRIAL IS NOT THE ROCK OR THE WATER...
...BUT YOUR PANIC, YOUR FEAR, YOUR MENTAL WEAKNESS!
HAA HAA (CHUFF)
KURDA WAS RIGHT.
I'M NOT CUT OUT FOR THIS...
ON YOUR FEET, DARREN!
GU (GRAB)
THAT HURTS! QUIT IT!
CHAPTER 36:
THE FIRST TRIAL
IMAGINE HOW MUCH SHARPER THE STAKES IN THE HALL OF DEATH ARE!
NOW GET TO WORK, IF YOU DON'T WANT TO DIE!
GOHHHH (WHOOOSH)

THE AQUATIC MAZE.
A MAN-MADE LABYRINTH WITH A LOW CEILING AND WATERTIGHT WALLS. THE WALLS ARE REMOVABLE, WHICH MEANS THE MAZE CAN BE ALTERED EACH TIME IT IS USED.
WATER IS PUMPED INTO THE MAZE AS THE TRIAL BEGINS, AND IT REACHES THE CEILING SHORTLY AFTER FIFTEEN MINUTES.
IT'S A RACE AGAINST TIME TO REACH ONE OF THE FOUR EXITS, ONE FOR EACH EDGE OF THE MAZE, BEFORE YOU SUFFOCATE.
CHAPTER 36:
THE FIRST TRIAL
THE EXITS ARE MARKED WITH A WHITE X.
WHEN THE BLACK SWITCH IN THE MIDDLE IS PRESSED, THE WATER DRAINS OUT AND THE TRIAL IS COMPLETE.
THE PROBLEM IS, THE CHALLENGER MUST DRAG AROUND A ROCK HALF HIS WEIGHT.
THE COMBINATION OF ROCK AND WATER SLOWLY SAP BOTH MIND AND BODY.
THOSE WHO GIVE IN TO PANIC, HESITATION OR DESPAIR ...
...WILL DIE.

LOOK AT ALL OF YOUR SUPPORTERS, DARREN.
SUP-PORTERS? WHAT'S THAT GESTURE ?
I'VE SEEN KURDA DO THAT BEFORE.
IT IS THE DEATH'S TOUCH SIGN.
IT MEANS, "EVEN IN DEATH, MAY YOU BE TRIUMPHANT."
WE BELIEVE THAT THE GODS OF THE VAMPIRES RESPECT THOSE WHO DIE NOBLY.

A VAMPIRE OF GOOD STANDING...
A VAMPIRE OF GOOD STANDING ALWAYS PUTS THE NEEDS OF THE CLAN...
...BEFORE HIS OWN WELL-BEING.
THE HAND GESTURE IS TO REMIND YOU OF THAT.
DO YOU THINK I'LL EVER BE ONE, HARKAT?
THE VAMPIRES... ARE BETTING... ON THAT VERY... SUBJECT.
REALLY? WHICH OUTCOME ARE THEY BETTING ON?
MOST ARE BETTING... AGAINST YOU.
HA! THAT FIGURES.
BUT KURDA AND GAVNER... AND ARRA HAVE... BET THAT... YOU WILL SUCCEED.
WHAT ABOUT MR. CREPSLEY?
HE SAID... HE DOES NOT... BET.
ESPECIALLY NOT...ON CHILDREN.
THAT'S THE SORT OF THING THAT DRY OLD BUZZARD WOULD SAY.
BUT I...HEARD HIM SAY...THAT IF YOU...FAILED, HE WOULD...EAT HIS CAPE.

WHAT ARE YOU TWO TALKING ABOUT? FOCUS ON THE TASK AT HAND.
I KNOW.
DON'T WORRY, MR. CREPSLEY. YOU WON'T BE EATING ANY CAPES.
I'VE GOT IT UNDER CONTROL.
I CAN PASS THIS. IT'S A PIECE OF CAKE!

ZAWA (MURMUR)
ZAWA

IT'S HUGE!
A FAR CRY FROM THAT TINY MODEL.
THERE THEY ARE...
ALL HERE FOR MY SAKE!
NOW BEGINS THE FIRST TRIAL OF INITIATION!
I, MIKA VER LETH, WILL OVER-SEE THIS TEST!
SHOW US THAT YOU ARE WORTHY, DARREN SHAN.
PROVE TO ME THAT MY OPINION OF YOU IS MISTAKEN.
GET GOING, DARREN!
MAY THE GODS BLESS YOU WITH THE LUCK OF THE VAMPIRES.
GYU (MMPH)

BLIND-FOLDED AND PUT ON A STRETCHER...
IT'S A LOT OF WORK JUST TO MAKE SURE I DON'T FIGURE OUT THE PATH WE'RE TAKING.
TO (TAP)

IT'S SO QUIET.
I CAN HEAR MY HEART-BEAT.
TO
TO
SETTLE DOWN. RELAX... CONCEN-TRATE.
DOKUN
DOKUN (BA-BUMP)
REMEMBER EACH AND EVERY THING THAT VANEZ TAUGHT YOU...
GOPOPO (BLUB BLUB)
WHEN THE WATER STARTS TO POUR IN...

...THAT'S THE SIGN TO BEGIN THE TRIAL!
SHURU (SWOOSH)
LISTEN TO ME, DARREN. THE MOST IMPORTANT THING...
...IS MAKING A MAP INSIDE YOUR HEAD!
EACH WALL, BIT OF FLOOR AND CEILING MAY LOOK THE SAME...
...BUT THEY AREN'T. YOU MUST FIND THE FLAWS!
A SPOT ON THE WALL.
A Y-SHAPED CRACK IN THE FLOOR.
A YELLOW STAIN BENEATH THE LAMP.
IT'S IMPORTANT TO GUIDE THE ROCK CAREFULLY.
IF IT GETS CAUGHT ON A CORNER, STOP AND WORK IT FREE. DON'T JUST TUG ON THE ROPE.
EVERY SECOND IS VITAL IN THE MAZE.

YES... THE MAP IS COMING TOGETHER IN MY HEAD.
VANEZ'S TRAINING IS PAYING OFF.
IF I KEEP UP THIS PACE, I'LL REACH THE EDGE OF THE MAZE SOON...

THE ROCK FEELS HEAVY, THOUGH.
MANY TIMES HEAVIER THAN AT PRACTICE...
GAKO (THUNK)
!!
IT MUST HAVE GOT STUCK.
GUI GUI (TUG)
JUST BE CALM...

WORK IT FREE... THERE!

ZAPAA (SPLASH)

WHERE AM I?

I WAS SO CONCENTRATED ON THE ROCK, I LOST FOCUS AND MY MIND WENT BLANK!

JABA (SLOSH)

DID I PASS THIS WAY BE-FORE? ANY NOTABLE MARKS?

BASHA (SPLASH)

I'M LOST!!!

I'VE GOT TO FIND THE EXIT!

I'M GOING TO...

SFX: BASHA (SPLASH) BASHA

... DIE ...

NO...

NOOOOOOOO!!!

SFX: HAA (HUFF) HAA

スー
SUU
ハー
HAA
スー
SUU (MMM)
THOSE WHO GIVE IN TO PANIC, HESITATION OR DESPAIR WILL DIE.
HAA
HAA
!!!
I'VE SEEN THAT MARKER BEFORE!
THE YELLOW STAIN BENEATH THE LAMP!
BASHA
BASHA
I STILL HAVE A CHANCE!
REBUILD THAT MAP!
ZAZAZA (SLOOOSH)
YOU CAN DO THIS, DARREN!

FU (HFF)
FU
IF IT COMES DOWN TO THE WIRE, THERE'S A LAST-CHANCE METHOD.
PICK UP THE ROCK AND SWIM WITH IT. IT'S VERY TAXING, BUT POSSIBLE TO DO.
YOU'LL WANT TO FINISH THE TRIAL WELL BEFORE RESORTING TO THAT, BUT IT'S THERE IF YOU NEED TO DO IT.
AND IT LOOKS LIKE I DO, VANEZ.
I'VE GOT FIVE OR SIX MIN-UTES OF BREATH, AT BEST.
GOT TO FIND AN EXIT BEFORE THEN!
NOT HERE... OR HERE.
IS THERE REALLY AN EXIT OUT OF THIS PLACE?
ZUSHI (OOMF)
I SHOULD HAVE REACHED THE OUTER WALL BY NOW.
GO (CRUNCH)

GABOBO (BLORCHH)
DAMN! LOST MY BREATH!
MY BREATH ...
NEED AIR! NOW!
!!?
THE WATER'S ...
...AT THE CEILING ...
THIS CAN'T BE HAPPEN-ING...
AM I GOING TO DIE HERE ...?

WHAT'S HAPPENING AT THE CIRQUE DU FREAK RIGHT NOW?
I WISH I COULD SEE EVRA AND THE OTHERS ONE MORE TIME...
I'M SORRY, SAM...
SORRY, DEBBIE ...
MUM, DAD...
ANNIE ...
I'M SO SORRY THAT I DIDN'T ...
...LIVE UP TO YOUR EXPECTATIONS.
YO!

A WHITE X!!
IS IT REAL, OR ARE MY EYES PLAYING TRICKS ON ME?
NO... IT DOESN'T MATTER WHAT IT IS...
GUGU (HRRG)
I'M NOT...
GARI (SCRAPE)

...GOING DOWN...

DAN (STOMP)
...WITH-OUT A FIGHT!!
REACH!!
REACH THE...
... SWI ...

YOU DID IT, DARREN! WELL DONE!
HA-HA! OH, GOOD. THE VAMPIRE GODS ARE PLEASED WITH ME...
STRANGE, THOUGH... I FEEL AS IF...
...I'VE HEARD THIS VOICE BEFORE...
UOOO (RAAAHH)
I CAN'T SEE ANYTHING, CAN'T FEEL ANYTHING... I WONDER IF THIS IS DEATH...
...DID I DIE AS BEFITTING AN HONOURABLE VAMPIRE OF GOOD STANDING?

YOU HAD ME ON THE EDGE OF MY SEAT!
YOU MAKE ONE HELL OF A VAMPIRE, DARREN!
THANKS...
I DID IT...
...AND IT WAS ALL THANKS TO YOU.
FIRST TRIAL, THE AQUATIC MAZE—CLEARED!!

CHAPTER 37:
THE SECOND TRIAL
AND JUST WHEN I THOUGHT I WAS TRULY A GONER...
...THERE WAS THAT WHITE X, FLOATING BEFORE MY EYES!!
I AM... GLAD YOU... SURVIVED.
ME TOO.
YOU WERE IN THERE NEARLY TEN MINUTES AFTER THE WATER REACHED THE TOP.
THE BETTING... AGAINST YOU...HAS DROPPED... SINCE YOU PASSED... THE FIRST TRIAL.
REALLY? GREAT!
HAVE YOU BET ANYTHING ON ME?
IF I HAD... ANYTHING TO BET... I WOULD.
HA HA HA!
MAYBE...MY CLOTHES...
HEY, DID YOU HEAR?
ONE OF THE FEW LATE-COMERS LEFT ARRIVED BEFORE DAWN, AND HE SAID...

...THAT VAMPANEZE TRACKS WERE SPOTTED ON THE WAY HERE.
CHAPTER 37:
THE SECOND TRIAL
ISN'T THAT WHAT GAVNER ALREADY REPORTED?
NOPE, DIFFERENT TRACKS, FOUND IN A DIFFERENT SPOT.
VANEZ...
I DON'T LIKE IT.
BUT WE'VE GOT TO CON-CENTRATE ON YOUR TRIALS.
LET'S MAKE OUR WAY TO THE HALL OF PRINCES.
GOT TO DRAW THE STONE FOR THE SECOND TRIAL...
GAYA (MURMUR)
GAYA

TWO DIFFERENT VAMPANEZE FOUND IN THE VICINITY OF VAMPIRE MOUNTAIN! THIS IS CAUSE FOR ALARM!
THEY'RE GOING TO START A WAR!
COULD THEY BE AGENTS OF THE VAMPANEZE LORD?
SFX: ZAWA (MUTTER) ZAWA
THE VAMPANEZE LORD IS A MYTH, A LEGEND!
THE VAMPANEZE ARE LIKE US! THEY DO NOT WISH FOR WAR!
IT'S POSSIBLE THAT MR. TINY SENT WORD TO THE VAMPANEZE, AS HE DID TO US!
PERHAPS THE PAIR ON THE WAY HERE WERE TRYING TO WARN US, OR DISCUSS THE...
GAYA
GAYA
"VAMPANEZE" AND "DISCUSSION" ARE TOPICS THAT NEVER GO TOGETHER!

GAYA (MURMUR)
GAYA
GAYA
THERE YOU ARE.
YOU DID WELL, YOUNG SHAN.
THERE'S A LONG WAY TO GO, BUT I'M WILLING TO ACCEPT THAT I MIGHT HAVE BEEN WRONG ABOUT YOU.
TH-THANK YOU, MIKA.
I MUST APOLOGIZE THAT THE MATTER OF THE VAM-PANEZE IS PREOCCU-PYING US, DARREN.
YOU MUST TELL US OF YOUR EXPLOITS IN THE MAZE AT A LATER TIME.
NOW, CHOOSE A STONE.
GOSO (RUSTLE)
GOSO
NUMBER TWENTY-THREE! THE SECOND TRIAL SHALL BE...
...THE PATH OF NEEDLES!!
GYU (SQUEEZE)
23*
GAYA
GAYA
PATH OF NEEDLES? SOUNDS PAINFUL.
YOU'LL FIND OUT ONCE WE PRACTICE IT.

I THINK...
...WE'LL HAVE ARRA COME AND HELP WITH THIS PRACTICE SESSION.
GAYA
GAYA
ZAWA (MUTTER)
ZAWA
GAYA
GAYA
THE CONFUSION AND CONSTERNATION OVER THE APPROACH OF THE VAMPANEZE HAD NOT DIED OUT...
...BY THE TIME MY SECOND TRIAL BEGAN.
BEGIN THE SECOND TRIAL, THE PATH OF NEEDLES!!

YESTERDAY'S PRACTICE LEFT ME EXHAUSTED, BUT I FEEL FRESH AND ENERGIZED TODAY!
BU (GRRK)
BUSHU (BSSHT)
LIKE WITH THE AQUATIC MAZE, VANEZ IS GIVING ME JUST THE RIGHT AMOUNT OF TRAINING FOR MY TRIAL!
HE'S FAMOUS FOR A REASON!
THERE'S STILL MUCH MORE AHEAD, THOUGH...
I'LL PASS AS SOON AS I'VE CROSSED IT...
...BUT THIS ONE WILL PROBABLY TAKE A WHILE.
OF COURSE, THIS ONE SHOULD BE EASIER THAN THE MAZE—YOU'VE GOT NO TIME LIMIT!
SOOO (SHHH)
EASY FOR YOU TO SAY, VANEZ...
THE STALAGMITES ARE VERY SHARP AND PAINFUL, BUT YOU'VE GOT TO GRIP THEM FIRMLY.
OTHERWISE YOU'LL END UP LOSING YOUR BALANCE AND IMPALE YOURSELF IN THE FLICKER OF AN EYE.
GOKU (GULP)

DON'T BE A COWARD! YOU BEAT THAT WATER TRIAL!
YOU CAN EASILY CROSS THIS PATH OF NEEDLES!!
BI (RIP)
SFX: GU.. (RRGH)
REMEMBER TO MOVE CAREFULLY, DARREN. THOSE STALAGMITES CAN BREAK EASILY.
AND AS QUIETLY AS POSSIBLE...
SOUNDS AND VIBRATIONS WILL BE THE END OF YOU.
SU (SHH)
EVEN THE SMALLEST NOISES WILL REACH THE STALACTITES ABOVE, ECHOING UNTIL THEY RESULT...
DON (BOOM)
ON (OOM)
UON (OMM)

BIN (BING)
YURA (WOBBLE)
BIN
YURA
POKI (SNAP)
HYUOOO (WHOOOSH)
...IN A CASCADE ...
ZASHU (SLASH)
...OF NEEDLE-SHARP BLADES !!
ZAZA (ZZSHH)
DO (DMM)
BI (ZZKK)
DOSU (THWAM)

I SEE... SO THAT'S WHAT SHE MEANT.
HAA (HUFF)
HAA
CONCEN-TRATE ...
MUST KEEP FOCUS ...
SUPPOSE I'M HALFWAY ACROSS BY NOW.
UGH, I'M A MESS.
ZUTA (ZLUGH)
MY WHOLE BODY HURTS.
IF I WASN'T A HALF-VAMPIRE, I'D HAVE DIED OF BLOOD LOSS LONG AGO.
GOSHI (RUB)
GOSHI

THE BLOOD IS SLICK...
ONCE I'VE FINISHED THIS TRIAL ...
...I'LL TAKE ANOTHER SHOWER IN THE HALL OF PERTA VIN-GRAHL. THINK OF HOW RE-FRESHING THAT'LL BE...
HEH HEH
BACK ON THE MOVE...
GU (HRGG)
YOU NEED LUCK TO SURVIVE THE AQUATIC MAZE, BUT NOT IN THE PATH OF NEEDLES!
YOU HOLD YOUR LIFE IN YOUR OWN HANDS!
YOU HAVE AN EXCELLENT SENSE OF BALANCE.
I KNOW YOU CAN BEAT THIS TRIAL!
HAA (HUFF)
HAA

HAA
HAA
GU (TUG)
GU
GOOD...
...IT'S NOT BREAKING.
GU
BOKI (CRACK)
GURA (SLIP)
GURU (SPIN)
DON (THWAM)

U... (RGH)
UU... (UNGG)
GOKU (BLUP)
GOKU
AAAGH!
UON (WOOM)
UON
POKI (CRAK)
POKI (CRAK)
DO (DMM)
DOZU (DSHH)
OH NO... I HAVE TO MOVE FROM THIS SPOT...
...BUT MY CLOTHES ARE SNAGGED!

IF THAT HUGE STALACTITE SHOULD FALL ON ME...
UON
UON
BIRI (ZZD)
BIRI
DON'T FALL...
DON'T YOU DARE...
PISHI (SNIP)
PLEASE, PLEASE...
BOGI (GRRNCH)

AAH!
GUH!
Y'GUI
GUI (TUG)
I CAN'T DO IT...
GOOU (WHOOOSH)
I CAN'T GET OUT OF THE WAY!
GO (GWOMM)

DOSHU
(DSHHH)

HOW LONG HAS IT BEEN SINCE THE START, VANEZ?
WE JUST PASSED NINETY MINUTES.
MOST VAMPIRES ARE DONE IN LESS THAN FORTY, BUT DARREN IS A HALF-VAMPIRE.
HE'LL BE JUST FINE, LARTEN.
ALL WE CAN DO IS TRUST THAT HE WILL EMERGE.
DARREN...

HAA (HUFF)
ハァ
HAA
ハァ
RRGH... NNG!
HA... HA HA HA!
SOOO (SHHH)
I'M...
...I'M ALIVE...
ZU (MMPH)
ズッ
ZAWA (MURMUR)
ザワッ
AHA!
THERE HE IS!!

HAA
HAA
YOTA (TRUDGE)
YOTA
WAAA (RAHHH)
PASA (FLAP)
LOOKS LIKE IT WASN'T THE CAKEWALK YOU WERE EXPECTING!
HA HA...
YOUR CUTS AND GASHES ARE DEEP, DARREN.
I HOPE THAT YOU CAN HEAL BEFORE THE NEXT TRIAL.
WE CAN GIVE HIM SOME BALMS AND BAN-DAGES.
I'VE GOT FORTY-EIGHT HOURS UNTIL THE NEXT ONE. THERE'S NO WAY THESE WILL HEAL IN TIME...
GREAT NEWS, DARREN!

THE FESTIVAL OF THE UNDEAD BEGINS TOMORROW!!
IS THAT TRUE?
THE FINAL VAMPIRE JUST ARRIVED FOR THE COUNCIL.
CONGRATULATIONS! YOU MADE IT.
YOU LOOK WORSE FOR THE WEAR, HOWEVER...
THEY'RE ONLY CUTS. THEY'LL HEAL.
THIS IS PERFECT TIMING. THINGS COULDN'T HAVE WORKED OUT BETTER IF WE'D PLANNED THEM.
NO KIDDING! THREE NIGHTS TO DRINK, BE MERRY, RECOVER, AND RELAX!!
UOO (RAHH)
I SURE HOPE I'M READY IN TIME...
SECOND TRIAL, THE PATH OF NEEDLES— CLEARED!!

I KNOW ALL OF YOU HAVE HEARD THE RUMOURS OF THE VAMPANEZE. BUT THE NEXT THREE NIGHTS ARE FOR ENJOYING THE FESTIVAL OF THE UNDEAD.
IT IS GOOD TO SEE YOU, MY FRIENDS. WE WELCOME YOU ALL TO VAMPIRE MOUNTAIN!
CHAPTER 38:
THE FESTIVAL BEGINS

BUT BEFORE WE BEGIN...
...THE ROLL CALL OF THOSE WHO'VE PASSED ON TO PARADISE SINCE LAST WE MET FOR COUNCIL.
MY WOUNDS FROM THE PATH OF NEEDLES ITCH AS THEY HEAL...
IT'S A GOOD THING THE FESTIVAL STARTED, SO I HAVE THREE EXTRA DAYS TO GET BETTER.
SEE ME LATER, DARREN. I HAVE SOMETHING TO EASE THE ITCHING.
GREAT! THANK YOU, SEBA!
MAKE THE DEATH'S TOUCH SIGN, DARREN.
NINE NAMES HAVE BEEN CALLED.
EVEN IN DEATH, MAY THEY BE TRIUMPHANT.
THAT IS THE LAST PIECE OF OFFICIAL BUSINESS!
THE FESTIVAL BEGINS. LUCK TO YOU, MY FRIENDS!
LUCK!
LUCK!
LUCK!
AND THAT WAS THE BEGINNING OF THE GRAND FESTIVAL OF THE UNDEAD!

THE THREE GAMING HALLS WERE IN A STATE OF ABSOLUTE BEDLAM!
WAA (RAHHH)
UOUU (ROARR)
EVERY-ONE WAS ITCHING TO FIGHT WITH THEIR FRIENDS AND RIVALS.
EVEN THE USUALLY RESERVED MR. CREPSLEY TOOK PART IN THE BRAWLS.
I COULD SEE GAVNER AND VANEZ AMONG THE THRONG.
AND EVEN ELDERLY VAMPIRES LIKE SEBA AND PARIS WERE RIGHT IN THE THICK OF IT!
IT'S A FESTIVAL RULE THAT IF ANYONE SHOULD CHALLENGE YOU TO COMBAT, YOU CAN'T REFUSE THEM.
IT EVEN APPLIES TO HALF-VAMPIRES AND LITTLE PEOPLE!

PAN (CLAP)
PAN
OOH!
I CAN'T DRINK... ANOTHER DROP...
BESIDES... I'M STILL... UNDERAGE...
FURA
FURA (WOBBLE)
HA-HA! HAVE THEY BEEN FORCING YOU TO DRINK, DARREN?
KURDA!
CRAZY, ISN'T IT? ALL THESE VAMPIRES, ACTING LIKE WILD CHILDREN.
THINK HOW EMBARRASSING IT WOULD BE IF ANYONE SAW US!
HA-HA! IT'S FUN THOUGH, ISN'T IT?
AT LEAST I ONLY HAVE TO ENDURE IT ONCE EVERY TWELVE YEARS.
HOW ABOUT IT, KURDA? LIKE YOUR CHANCES?

NONE OF THAT COWARD'S TALK, KURDA!
WA (RAHH)
I HAVE A SORE LEG, ARRA...YOU KNOW I WOULDN'T STAND A CHANCE.
COME ON, KURDA. NOT EVEN A PACIFIST LIKE YOU HAS THE RIGHT TO REFUSE A CHALLENGE DURING THE FESTIVAL OF THE UNDEAD.
I'VE BEEN WAITING FOR DECADES TO GET YOU UP HERE.
OOO (OOOHHH)
I'LL HAVE TO HOPE THAT SHE GOES EASY ON ME, THEN.
ARRA HASN'T LOST AT THE BARS IN ELEVEN YEARS!
YOU'RE GOING TO ACCEPT?
I HOPE IT PROVES WORTH THE WAIT, THEN.
THERE WAS NO WAY KURDA COULD BEAT ARRA.
BUT THE MATCH TOOK AN UNEXPECTED TURN...
BACHII (SWAPP)
YOU CAN'T DO THIS, KURDA ...

DAN! (WHAM)
WELL DONE, KURDA! EXCELLENT SHOWING!
CAN IT BE? ARRA LOST!?
ARE YOU OKAY, ARRA?
YOU CHEATED! YOU FAKED INJURY!
KI (GRR)
THERE'S NO RULE AGAINST THAT. I BEAT YOU FAIR AND SQUARE.
YOU SHOULDN'T HAVE LEAPT IN FOR THE KILL LIKE THAT.
IF YOU HADN'T BEEN SO EAGER TO DISGRACE ME, MY TRICK WOULDN'T HAVE WORKED.
GU (MMPH)
THERE IS TRUTH IN YOUR WORDS. WILL YOU FORGIVE ME?
PIKU (TWITCH)
I WILL IF YOU'LL TAKE MY HAND.

DA (DASH)
ARRA!
...BUT I CANNOT BRING MYSELF TO TAKE IT.
I CAN-NOT.
YOU BEAT ME CLEANLY, AND IT SHAMES ME TO REFUSE YOUR HAND...
SFX: ZAWA (MURMUR) ZAWA
I FEEL SORRY FOR HER. IT MUST BE CRUEL TO BE SO SET IN ONE'S WAYS.
HER REFUSAL TO SHAKE MY HAND WILL HAUNT HER FOR THE REST OF HER LIFE.
I THOUGHT YOU WEREN'T SUPPOSED TO BE ANY GOOD WHEN IT CAME TO FIGHTING
I CHOOSE NOT TO FIGHT— IT DOESN'T MEAN I CAN'T!
I'M NO HEROIC VAMPIRE, BUT I'M NOT THE USELESS COWARD MANY THINK I AM.
IF YOU FOUGHT MORE OFTEN, THEY WOULDN'T THINK THAT.
TRUE...
...BUT THEIR OPINION DOESN'T MATTER.
......

IN THE HEART IS WHERE A MAN SHOULD JUDGE HIMSELF, NOT ON BARS OR IN A RING OR ON A BATTLEFIELD.
IF YOU KNOW IN YOUR HEART THAT YOU'RE TRUE AND BRAVE, THAT SHOULD BE ENOUGH.
DOSA (THUMP)
OF THE NINE VAMPIRES WHO'VE DIED SINCE LAST COUNCIL...
...FIVE COULD HAVE BEEN HERE TONIGHT, ALIVE AND WELL...
...HAD THEY NOT BEEN DETERMINED TO PROVE THEMSELVES TO OTHERS.
THEY DROVE THEMSELVES TO EARLY GRAVES, JUST SO THEIR COMPANIONS WOULD ADMIRE THEM.
IT'S STUPID.
POINTLESS AND SAD.
UOOOO (RAHHHH)
AND ONE NIGHT IT MAY PROVE TO BE THE END OF US ALL...

ザワ
ZAWA (MURMUR)
ザワ
ZAWA
ARE YOU ENJOY-ING YOUR-SELVES?
LOOK AT YOUR SCRATCHES AND BRUISES ...
HE (HEH) HE
HA-HA! I'VE NOT BEEN ACTING MY AGE!
THINGS HAVE FINALLY CALMED DOWN SOME-WHAT.
I THOUGHT WE COULD GO AND SEE TO YOUR ITCHING NOW.
REALLY? GREAT!
GRAB THAT BEAUTIFUL SPIDER OF YOURS— MADAM OCTA.
WHY?
WEREN'T YOU SPEND-ING TIME MAKING A MAP, KURDA?
WE'RE GOING TO VISIT A LOCATION YOU MIGHT FIND INTERESTING.
I'D LOVE TO COME!

FASCINATING! I'VE NEVER SEEN THESE TUNNELS!
ｶﾘ...
KARI (SCRITCH)
I DON'T KNOW WHAT THE APPEAL IN MAP-MAKING IS...
IT IS A USEFUL SKILL. YOU SHOULD TRY IT, GAVNER.
ME, WASTE MY TIME MAKING MAPS? NO THANKS.
GAVNER'S NOT CUT OUT FOR SUCH PRECISE AND FUSSY WORK!
KURDA'S MAPS HAVE HAD GREAT PRACTICAL BENEFIT TO US, HOWEVER.
TAKE THE BREACH POINTS, FOR EXAMPLE.
BREACH POINTS?
TUNNELS THAT LEAD RIGHT INTO THE HALLS OF VAMPIRE MOUNTAIN.
THERE ARE MANY WAYS INTO THE HALLS BESIDES THE MAIN GATES OF ENTRY.
KURDA HAS UNEARTHED MANY OF THESE AND BROUGHT THEM TO OUR ATTENTION...
...SO THAT WE MIGHT SEAL THEM OFF AGAINST ATTACK.
WHO'D ATTACK YOU UP HERE?
STRAY WOLVES, RATS AND BATS OFTEN CREEP IN AND FORAGE FOR FOOD.

OKAY, I WAS WRONG!
YOUR MAPS DO SERVE A PURPOSE!
HA HA HA!
THEY WERE GETTING TO BE A NUISANCE. SO WE WERE FINALLY ABLE TO PUT A STOP TO THEIR ADVANCES.
WITH MY MAPS, OF COURSE!
NO, KURDA. NO CANDLES.
I'LL GET OUT A CANDLE.
WE'VE COME RATHER DEEP. IT'S PITCH-BLACK HERE...
KASA (SCUTTLE)
WE DO NOT WANT TO DISTURB THE RESIDENTS.
KASA
KASA
KASASA (SCUTTLE)

KASA (SKITTER)
WHAT'S THERE?
KASA
BOTORI (PLOP)
MUZU (ITCH)
I WOULD ADVISE AGAINST SNEEZING.
THEY MIGHT INTERPRET THAT AS A SIGN OF AGGRES-SION.
AAH...
AAH...
THESE SPIDERS ARE POISON-OUS.
ALONE, THEY ARE HARMLESS, BUT IF THEY ATTACK IN GROUPS...
...EVEN A VAMPIRE WILL BE IN FOR DIRE CONSE-QUENCES.
KASA
KASASA (SCUTTLE)
THESE CREATURES HAVE BEEN HERE FOR MILLENNIA. WE CALL THEM BA'HALEN'S SPIDERS...
...AFTER THE VAMPIRE WHO BROUGHT THEM HERE, IF LEGENDS ARE TO BE BELIEVED.
KASASA
MADAM OCTA...
MOZO (RUSTLE)

L-LET'S BEAT IT. I WANT OUT OF HERE!
NOT SO FAST, MY FRIENDS. THESE SPIDERS ARE WHY WE'RE HERE.
PURU PURU (SHIVER)
OOOH!
GUSHI (SQUISH)
GUSHI
DARREN— TAKE OFF YOUR SHIRT.
WHOA! I CAN FEEL THE ITCHING FADING AWAY ALREADY...
THERE ARE CHEMICALS IN THESE COBWEBS WHICH AID THE HEALING PROCESS AND WORK AGAINST IRRITATION.
WHY HAVE I NEVER HEARD OF SUCH A THING?
BECAUSE I DO NOT TELL ANY-ONE.
IF EVERYONE KNEW OF IT, THE SUPPLY WOULD RUN OUT AND THE SPIDERS WOULD MOVE ELSE-WHERE.
I ONLY BRING PEOPLE HERE WHEN THEY TRULY NEED HELP...
...AND I ALWAYS ASK THEM TO KEEP THE SECRET TO THEM-SELVES.
MAY I TRUST YOU TO KEEP IT TOO?

SU (SHH)
DARREN'S QUITE HANDY WITH THAT FLUTE.
COULD I CONTROL THEM TOO?
IT IS MORE DIFFICULT THAN IT LOOKS.
VERY FEW PEOPLE HAVE THE ABILITY TO BOND WITH SPIDERS.
DARREN IS A TALENTED YOUNG MAN.

THE ITCHING IS GONE!
I THINK I'LL BE READY FOR THE NEXT TRIAL SOON!
AHH, THAT IS GOOD TO HEAR.
I SEE... SO THIS CONNECTS HERE...
!
DARREN, WE SHOULD BE CLOSE TO THE HALL OF FINAL VOYAGE, WHICH I MENTIONED TO YOU EARLIER.
WOULD YOU LIKE TO STOP BY?
REALLY? CAN I SEE IT?
OOO... (WHOOOSH)
GOOOOO (WHOOOOSH)
THIS PLACE IS SO GLOOMY...
IT'S DIFFERENT FROM THE HALL OF DEATH.
IT'S MY FIRST VISIT AS WELL.

IN AGES PAST, WE SENT OUR DEAD DOWN TO THIS RIVER TO BE WASHED OUT INTO NATURE.
GOHHHH (WHOOOSH)
BUT AFTER A TIME, THE BODIES GOT STUCK AND PILED UP IN THE RIVER.
WE HAVE SINCE STOPPED USING IT.
THE CURRENT IS MUCH TOO STRONG FOR EVEN A VAMPIRE TO SWIM AGAINST.
WE HAD A TEAM OF VAMPIRES ON ROPES FLOATING DOWN TO THE BLOCKAGE TO RIP THE BODIES FREE AND SEND THEM ALONG.
ZAZAA (SLOOOSH)
ISN'T IT A BAD THING FOR THEM TO BE RE-TURNED TO NATURE?
I THOUGHT VAMPIRE BLOOD WAS POISON-OUS TO ANIMALS.
ZO (SHIVER)
FIRST, THE BLOOD IS DRAINED AND THE ORGANS REMOVED ...
... BY THE GUARD-IANS OF THE BLOOD.
THOSE ARE REGULAR HUMANS THAT LIVE AMONG US HERE IN VAMPIRE MOUNTAIN.
REGULAR HUMANS ?
THOSE PEOPLE I SAW!
KOSO... (SNEAK)

YOU'VE SEEN THEM, DARREN? THEY'RE GHOULS...
THAT IS UNFAIR, GAVNER.
THEY WORK FAITHFULLY TO PREPARE THE DEAD AND PROVIDE US WITH BLOOD.
BLOOD? THEN ALL THE HUMAN BLOOD THAT IS DRUNK HERE...
...COMES FROM THEM, YES.
(WHOOOOSH)
THE GUARDIANS OF THE BLOOD AND THE VAMPIRES HAVE A SYMBIOTIC RELATIONSHIP.
THEY PROVIDE US WITH BLOOD, AND WE PROVIDE THEM WITH THE GUTS OF OUR DEAD TO EAT.
WE EXIST TOGETHER IN PERFECT HARMONY.
(WHOOOSH)
THIS IS A REALM OF THE DEAD, NOT THE LIVING.
LET'S GET BACK TO THE FESTI-VAL.
YEAH! THE NIGHT'S NEARLY OVER.
YOU NEED YOUR REST TO MAKE IT THROUGH THE COUNCIL!

IF I DIE IN THE TRIALS...
...WILL MY DRAINED, HOLLOWED BODY BE SENT DOWN THE RIVER?
BATTERED BY THE CURRENT, CARRIED FARTHER AND FARTHER AWAY FROM VAMPIRE MOUNTAIN...
...FARTHER AND FARTHER AND FARTHER...
BUN (SHAKE)
BUN
AS I LEFT THE HALL OF FINAL VOYAGE, I HOPED NEVER TO RETURN...
...NOT KNOWING THAT I WOULD SOON BE BACK, NOT TO MOURN THE PASSING OF SOMEBODY ELSE'S LIFE...
GOOO (WHOOOOSH)
TA (TEK)
...BUT TO FIGHT DESPERATELY FOR MY OWN!

...THE FESTIVAL OF THE UNDEAD REACHED THE END OF ITS THIRD NIGHT.
FIGHTING, SINGING, DANCING, CON-VERSING ...
IT WAS ALL THANKS TO SEBA AND HIS BA'HALEN'S SPIDERS.
BY THE TIME THE FESTIVITIES CONCLUDED WITH A GRAND, ELABORATE CEREMONY, MY WOUNDS HAD HEALED COM-PLETELY.

CHAPTER 39: THE THIRD TRIAL

THIS TIME, THE TRIAL THAT I PICKED FROM THE SACK WAS...
NOW I'VE GOT TO FOCUS ON THE THIRD TRIAL!

THE HALL OF FLAMES !!?
PEACE, LARTEN, PLEASE.
FORGIVE MY OUT-BURST. THIS IS GRAVE NEWS.
IT'S BAD, ISN'T IT?
YES. IT WILL BE YOUR HARDEST TRIAL YET.
YOU'LL LET ME HELP AGAIN, OF COURSE.
SU (SHH)
ARRA ...
YOUR ARM...
I AM ASHAMED OF MY ACTIONS IN THE HALL OF SPORT.

I OVER-ESTIMATED MY OWN STRENGTH.
MY PRIDE LED TO CARELESS-NESS, AND THAT WILL LEAD TO DEATH.
BUT IF YOU CAN AVOID BEING CARELESS, YOU WILL ALWAYS FIND A PATH TO VICTORY EVEN IN THE MOST DIFFICULT OF CIRCUMSTANCES.
A LESSON YOU CAN APPLY TO THIS TRIAL.
YOUR HELP IS APPRE-CIATED, ARRA.
WITH HER HELP, YOU MIGHT PULL THROUGH, DARREN.
THANK YOU, ARRA!
IT'S MY PLEASURE.
ARRA ...
LEAVE IT TO ME.
LET'S GET TRAINING THEN! THERE'S NOT A MOMENT TO WASTE!
R-RIGHT!
OF ALL THE TRIALS HE COULD HAVE PICKED...
I SPENT MOST OF THE FOLLOW-ING DAY AND NIGHT LEARNING TO DODGE FIRE.
GOOO (WHOOFF)

THE RULES OF THE HALL OF FLAMES WERE SIMPLE.
ALL YOU HAD TO DO WAS DODGE THE FLAMES THAT WERE PUMPED THROUGH THE HOLES ALL OVER THE ROOM.
GOOOO (WHOOOFFF)
BUT THE FIRE WAS UNPREDICT-ABLE, AND THERE WAS NO WAY TO TELL WHICH HOLES IT WOULD COME FROM.
IF YOU COULD SURVIVE IN THE HALL FOR FIFTEEN MIN-UTES WITHOUT BURNING TO A CRISP, YOU WOULD PASS THE TRIAL.
BO (BFF)
YEOW!
USE YOUR EARS, DARREN!
YOU CAN HEAR THE FLAMES COMING BEFORE YOU SEE THEM!
LISTEN CAREFULLY. YOU HEAR THE HISSING?
SHUUUU (HISSSSS)
YES...
THAT IS THE SOUND OF THE FLAMES PASSING NEARBY.
IT'S WHEN YOU HEAR A SHORT WHIS-TLING SOUND...
SHU (FFT)

GOU (WHOOFF)
LIKE THAT!
GUI (SNAG)
BOFU (BFF)
I...I THINK I GET THE IDEA...
COME THE TIME OF YOUR TRIAL, THERE WILL BE FIVE TIMES THE FLAME.
ONE GOOD BLAST, AND YOU'LL BE DEAD ON THE SPOT.
MOVE AS LITTLE AS POSSIBLE, AND CONCENTRATE ON LISTENING.
PREDICT WHERE THE FLAMES WILL COME FROM AND MOVE BEFORE THEY ARRIVE.
B-BUT CAN I REALLY DO IT ...?
NEVER DOUBT YOURSELF!
YOU WILL DO IT!
UNDERSTOOD?
GOKU (GULP)

MY PRACTICE CONTINUED WITHOUT REST, AND BEFORE I KNEW IT...
...IT WAS TIME FOR THE TRIAL.
THEY SEEM DIFFERENT THIS TIME...
IT MUST BE A MARK OF HOW SERIOUS THIS TRIAL IS...
GAKU (SHIVER)
GAKU
STOP SHAKING...
STOP SHAKING!!
BURU (SHAKE)
BURU
I'M SORRY NONE OF THE PRINCES COULD MAKE IT LAST TIME.
ARE YOU READY?
......
YES ...

MR. CREPSLEY, IF I DON'T PULL THROUGH, I WANT YOU TO...
DO NOT TALK LIKE THAT! THINK POSITIVELY!
I *AM* THINKING POSITIVELY...
...BUT I KNOW HOW DIFFICULT IT WILL BE.
I'M JUST SAYING, I'VE BEEN THINKING IT OVER...
...AND IF I DIE, I'D LIKE YOU TO TAKE MY BODY HOME AND BURY IT IN MY GRAVE.
THAT WAY I'LL BE CLOSE TO MUM, DAD, AND ANNIE.
VERY WELL.
MAY THE LUCK OF THE VAMPIRE GODS BE WITH YOU.
TA (STEP)

I'M PROUD TO HAVE BEEN...
...YOUR ASSISTANT.
GATAN (THUD)
I'LL BE RIGHT BACK!
BA (MMPH)
DAR-REN...

JUUU
(FZZZ)
I FEEL THE HEAT ...
TARA
(DRIP)
MY BREATH IS CAUGHT IN MY THROAT ...
MUKU
(PUFF)
I JUST HAVE TO DODGE ONE FLAME.
HAA
(HUFF)
HAA
THAT WILL RELEASE THE TEN-SION...
...AND FIFTEEN MINUTES LATER, I'LL BE DONE.
SHUUUUU
(HSSSS)
THAT'S THE VENT THE FLAME IS COMING FROM!
I'M FINE...I'VE GOT ENOUGH DIS-TANCE THAT I DON'T NEED TO MOVE.
SHU
(WHUFF)

DAN (LEAP)
DOGONN!! (KABOOOM)
COME THE TIME OF YOUR TRIAL, THERE WILL BE FIVE TIMES THE FLAME!
JIRI (WINCE)
JIRI
THIS IS RIDICULOUS...
THAT'S NO PLAIN OLD "FLAME"...
...IT'S AN EXPLOSION!
BOGOOO (BWABOOM)
DOOOO (BOOOM)

GATA (SHIVER)
GATA
I MUST NOT DOUBT MYSELF.
GYU (CLENCH)
I HAVE TO DO IT...
PAN (SMACK)
PAN
...OR I'M DEAD!!!
GOWA (GWRSHH)
SHUUU
SHIIU (HSSS)
SHII

DOGOO (KABOOM)
JA (SZZZ)
BOU (BWFF)
DON'T LET THE PAIN AFFECT YOU. SMALL BURNS WILL KEEP YOU FROM SUFFERING LARGE ONES.
NOBODY MAKES IT THROUGH THE HALL OF FLAMES UNMARKED.
IT'S TOO HOT!
MINIMIZE YOUR MOVEMENT AND MAKE DECISIONS INSTANTLY.
I'M SCARED!
IT HURTS!
DOJUU (FZZZ)
ALWAYS BE ON THE LOOKOUT FOR SPACE TO KEEP YOU FROM BEING SURROUNDED!

HOW MANY MINUTES HAVE PASSED?
FIVE? TEN? IT MIGHT NOT EVEN HAVE BEEN ONE YET.
GO (WHOOSH)
IT FEELS LIKE I'VE BEEN DODGING THE FLAMES FOR HOURS...
YORO (SLIP)
JU (FZZZ)
AGH!
!!!
OH NO!
STAY AWAY FROM THE CORNERS, DARREN! STICK TO THE MIDDLE AS MUCH AS POSSIBLE!

MOST WHO PERISH IN THE HALL OF FLAMES DO SO IN CORNERS, TRAPPED BY WALLS OF FIRE, UNABLE TO BREAK FREE.
GOKU (GULP)
SFX: DA (LEAP)
I'VE GOT TO GET BACK TO THE MIDDLE ...
SHU (FSHH)
BOOU (BWOOM)
A WALL OF FLAME !!
I'M TRAPPED!!
SHUUUU
DOKI (THUMP)

STUCK IN A CORNER.
THERE'S NO ESCAPE ...
MUST DECIDE NOW. MUST THINK OF WHAT I CAN DO.
HA... (HUFF)
HA...
THE CHOICE WITH THE HIGHEST POSSIBILITY OF SURVIVAL.
I'VE GOT TO BREAK THROUGH. DON'T TAKE THE FLAMES HEAD ON...
... BREAK THROUGH!
IT'S WHAT I NEED TO DO TO SURVIVE ...
I'M NOT AFRAID ...
DA (DASH)
JU (SZZZ)
BREAK THROUGH!
LEAP STRAIGHT THROUGH ...
...THE WALL OF FLAME !!!

BATA (FLOP)
BATA
BUSU (SZZ)
BUSU
SFX: KAHA (KHH)
KA (GAH)
MUST MOVE... NOW...
GUGU (RRRG)
...BEFORE THE NEXT... FLAMES COME...

DOSHA (DSHHH)

HURRY UP! HE MIGHT NOT... MUCH TIME!
SOMEONE GET... STRETCHER!
WHO'S... THERE? SOMEONE CAME... INSIDE...
WATCH OUT...THE TRIAL'S NOT... OVER YET...
M-MY GOODNESS...
...NEEDS MEDICAL ATTENTION!
MOVE! OUT OF THE WAY!
DARREN! DARR...
DO THEY... WANT TO BE BURNED? GET OUT... OF HERE...
THE FIRE... FIRE IS COMING... FIRE...
DARREN, IT IS OVER... IT IS OVER...
NO, DO NOT SPEAK...
THE FIFTEEN MINUTES ARE UP!

YOU WON.
MR... CREPSLEY...
HOW IS HE?
NOT GOOD.
BE CAREFUL WITH HIM!
THE POOR CHILD... HE CAN'T POSSIBLY BE READY FOR THE NEXT ONE...
...IN JUST FORTY-EIGHT HOURS. NOT AFTER THIS...

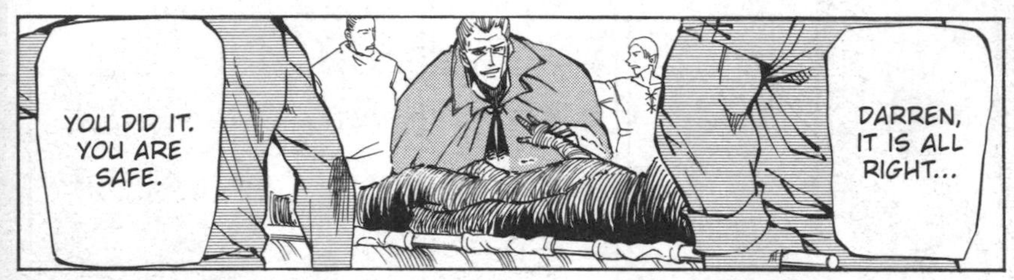
DARREN, IT IS ALL RIGHT...
YOU DID IT. YOU ARE SAFE.

WITH MY MIND CONSUMED BY A SEA OF FLAMES, A SWIRLING MAELSTROM OF RED AND YELLOW...
...THE SOUND OF MR. CREPSLEY'S KIND, SOFT VOICE ECHOED WITHIN MY HEAD...

CHAPTER 40:
MR. CREPSLEY'S HOPE

BATA
BATA (THUMP)
AAH... AAAAAH... AAGHHH...
I KNOW IT HURTS, DARREN!
BUT YOU MUST CONTAIN YOUR-SELF!
GOOO... (WHOOOSHH)
THIS... THIS IS HELL.
AN ENTIRE SEA OF FLAMES...
BURNING EVERY-THING... EVERY-ONE...
HUFF!
HUFF!
THIS IS MY FAULT.
HE IS SUF-FERING BECAUSE OF ME.
HE DOESN'T LOOK GOOD.
THE POOR BOY. HE MIGHT NOT...
THE FIRES...
...OF HELL...

AAH!

GATA (THUMP)
DARREN!
YOU ARE AWAKE AT LAST!

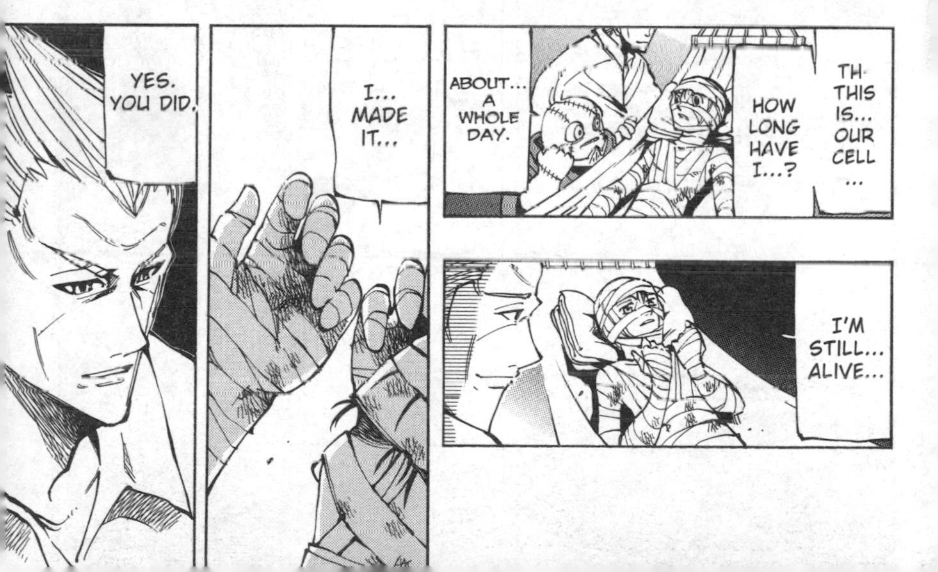
TH THIS IS... OUR CELL ...
HOW LONG HAVE I...?
ABOUT... A WHOLE DAY.
I'M STILL... ALIVE...
I... MADE IT...
YES. YOU DID.

HOW BAD... AM I BURNT?
カタ
KÁTA (THÚNK)
YOU LOOK... LIKE AN OVER... COOKED SAUSAGE.
OUCH!
HA-HA! VERY FUNNY...
YOU HAVE SUFFERED A TERRIBLE ORDEAL, BUT THE DAMAGE IS NOT PERMANENT.
YOUR FEET SUFFERED THE MOST, BUT THE MEDICS HAVE SAVED THEM.
YOUR HAIR, ON THE OTHER HAND, MIGHT NEVER GROW BACK.
WHAT ABOUT... NEXT TRIAL?
DO NOT THINK OF SUCH THINGS NOW.
I HAVE TO. WILL I...HAVE TIME...TO GET READY...FOR IT?
......
TELL ME... THE TRUTH.
THERE WILL BE NO EXTRA TIME.
KURDA IS IN THE HALL OF PRINCES AS WE SPEAK, ARGUING YOUR CASE.
BUT THERE WILL BE NO POST-PONE-MENT. THERE IS NO PRECE-DENT.
THOSE UNFIT TO CONTINUE MUST BE TAKEN TO...

PASA (FLAP)
I KNOW ...
...THE HALL OF... DEATH.
KA (TEK)
IS DARREN AWAKE?
IT'S ALMOST SUNSET!
YOU MUST CHOOSE YOUR NEXT TRIAL OR ADMIT FAILURE AND BE CARTED AWAY FOR EXECUTION.
GU CHRRG!?
IF WE CARRY YOU TO THE HALL OF PRINCES, DO YOU THINK YOU CAN STAND UPRIGHT FOR A FEW MINUTES?
KURDA, WHAT ARE YOU DOING?
JUST TRUST ME AND READY A STRETCH-ER, LARTEN!

ZAWA (MURMUR)
WHAT'S GOING ON, KURDA?
ZAWA
THERE'S NO WAY DARREN WILL BE READY TO FACE A TRIAL TOMORROW.
ARE YOU LISTENING TO ME?
GASHA (CLUNK)
UGH!
SHIIIN (SILENCE)

IS THIS YOUNG MASTER SHAN?
IT IS, SIRE.
HE LOOKS TER-RIBLE ...
ARE YOU SURE HE'S FIT TO CONTINUE WITH THE TRIALS?
HE IS MERELY RESTING, SIRE. HE LIKES TO PRETEND TO BE INJURED...
...SO THAT HE CAN BE CARRIED AROUND LIKE A LORD.
SFX: DOYO (SHOCK) DOYO
REALLY? IF THAT IS THE CASE, LET THE BOY STEP FORWARD AND CHOOSE HIS NEXT TRIAL.
HOW-EVER ...
...YOU UNDERSTAND WHAT WE MUST DO...
...IF HE IS UNABLE.
WE UNDER-STAND.
ON YOUR FEET, DARREN.
ZAWA
ZAWA
RRGH...

KURDA, HE CAN-NOT DO THIS!
IT IS IMPOS-SIBLE!
I'M SORRY...
I KNOW IT WILL BE HARD FOR YOU...
...BUT YOU MUST WALK UP AND CHOOSE YOUR TRIAL.
PLEASE...
RRSH...
FURA (LURCH)
FURA
YOTA (FLOP)
YOTA
NNG...
GASHA (CLACK)
NUM-BER FOUR!
THE BLOODED BOAR!!
ZAWA
ZAWA (MURMUR)

A TRICKY TRIAL. ARE YOU READY FOR IT, DARREN?
FURA (SWAY)
FURA
I WILL BE...THERE TO FACE IT... TOMORROW, AS...SCHED-ULED.
AHH.
THAT IS GOOD TO HEAR.
AHEM!
I, HOW-EVER, CANNOT MAKE IT.
I HAVE PRESSING BUSINESS TO ATTEND TO AND REGRET-FULLY MUST MISS THIS TRIAL.
PON (PAT)
MMPH...
MY GOOD COLLEAGUE, MIKA, WILL TAKE MY PLACE.
WHAT A SHAME, INDEED ...
ACTUALLY, I CAN'T GET AWAY FROM THE HALL TOMORROW EITHER. THIS VAMPANEZE LORD BUSINESS TAKES UP ALL MY TIME.
HOW ABOUT YOU, ARROW ?
......
ALAS, MY SCHEDULE IS ALSO FULL.
NIYA (GRIN)
SU (RISE)
?

SIRES, YOU HAVE ALREADY SKIPPED ONE OF DARREN'S TRIALS.
TO NEGLECT YOUR POST TWICE IN THE COURSE OF ONE SET OF TRIALS IS UNPARDON-ABLE!
THIS DOES DARREN A GRAVE DISSERVICE. I MUST PROTEST MOST STRONGLY.
MMM-HMM...
PARIS...
YES, YES! I SEE TRUTH IN YOUR WORDS.
VERY WELL. DARREN HAS REPORTED THAT HE IS FIT FOR HIS NEXT TRIAL.
ZA (ZSHH)
SINCE WE CANNOT BE THERE TO OVERSEE IT, WE WILL HAVE TO POSTPONE IT.
WE APOLOGIZE FOR THE INCONVENIENCE, DARREN. WILL YOU PARDON US FOR A SEVENTY-TWO-HOUR DELAY?

HEE HEE HEE!
BUT IF WE HAVE TO WAIT, WE WILL.
HEH HEH.
SFX: HAA (SIGH)
IT IS ANNOYING, SIRE. DARREN IS ANXIOUS TO FINISH HIS TRIALS.
WELL, I...
...I SUPPOSE I WOULDN'T MIND...
THE PRINCES WANTED TO HELP DARREN...
ACTUALLY, IT WAS PARIS'S IDEA.
YOU SCOUNDREL, KURDA SMAHLT! HOW DID YOU DREAM THAT ONE UP?
I NEVER TAUGHT YOU HOW TO PULL OFF THAT TRICK!
HA HA HA!

...BUT THEY COULDN'T TURN AROUND AND GIVE HIM SPECIAL TREATMENT.
THEY NEEDED AN EXCUSE TO SAVE FACE.
THIS WAY, IT LOOKS AS THOUGH DARREN WAS READY AND WILLING TO PROCEED...
...SO THERE'S NO SHAME IN POSTPONING IT.
SO THAT'S... WHY I HAD TO STAND.
SO NOBODY... WOULD BE SUSPICIOUS.
AND YOU DID VERY WELL.
THANKS FOR EVERYTHING...
... KURDA.
THREE DAYS...AND NIGHTS. WILL IT BE... ENOUGH?
IF NOT...
...IT WILL NOT BE FOR WANT OF TRYING.
YEAH.

OVER THE NEXT THREE NIGHTS, I FOCUSED ON HEALING MY BURNS.
THE WOUNDS WERE CLEANED, GIVEN LOTION TO SOOTHE THE BURNING, AND MY BANDAGES WERE CHANGED CONSTANTLY.
BETWEEN THE PAIN AND THE NIGHTMARES, I BARELY SLEPT A WINK.
LUCKILY, I HAD A CONSTANT STREAM OF VISITORS...
...TO DISTRACT ME FROM THE PAIN.
HERE'S MR. TOAST HIMSELF!
NO... MR. SAUSAGE.
HE LOOKS MORE LIKE TOAST!
EVEN IF THEY HAD TO USE BAD JOKES TO DO IT.
SEBA GAVE ME EVERY SOOTHING BALM HE COULD THINK OF.
THAT STINGS
VANEZ DISCUSSED THE NEXT TRIAL WITH ME.
THERE ARE NO SPECIAL SKILLS REQUIRED FOR THE BLOODED BOAR.
YOU'LL JUST BE FIGHTING TO THE DEATH.
YOU'LL BE BETTER SERVED BY RESTING AND HEALING UP.
KURDA WAS VERY BUSY WITH THE MEETINGS ABOUT THE VAMPANEZE, BUT WE HAD SOME VERY INTERESTING CONVERSATIONS THE FEW TIMES HE DID COME AROUND.
FOR THE FIRST TIME, THEY'RE SERIOUSLY TALKING ABOUT MAKING PEACE WITH THE VAMPANEZE.

UNLESS WE ACT QUICKLY TO PREVENT THE POSSIBILITY OF A VAMPANEZE LORD ARISING, HE'LL COME.
STOPPING HIM BEFORE HE GETS STARTED MAY TAKE SACRIFICE, BUT IF THAT'S THE PRICE OF AVERTING A WAR, SO BE IT.
HOW DO YOU FEEL, DARREN?
ARRA!
......
I SHOULD BE GOING NOW.
GATA (THUMP)
WAIT.
I WANT TO THANK YOU FOR WHAT YOU DID FOR DARREN.
IT WAS NOTHING.
I DON'T AGREE WITH YOUR WAYS—THERE'S A THIN LINE BETWEEN DIPLOMACY AND COWARDICE.
BUT ONLY YOU HAD SENSE ENOUGH TO STEER HIM TO SAFETY IN HIS HOUR OF NEED.
THANK YOU, KURDA.

YOU HAVE MY THANKS AS WELL.
SURE, LARTEN.
DO YOU KNOW, THAT'S THE CLOSEST SHE'LL EVER GET TO SAYING SHE LIKES ME.
THEY TALKED ABOUT THE OLD NIGHTS AND THEIR LIFE TOGETHER WHEN THEY WERE MATES.
...THOUGH SHE SPENT MORE TIME TALKING WITH MR. CREPSLEY THAN ME.
ARRA OFTEN CAME TO SEE ME...
SEEYA SOON, ARRA.
I'LL SEE YOU AGAIN SOON.
YOU'RE LOOKING MUCH BETTER, DARREN.
HA HA.
ほわ
HOWA (GLOW)
WHAT WILL THAT MEAN FOR ME, HIS APPRENTICE?
ARE THEY PLANNING TO MATE AGAIN SOON?

PACHI
(POP)
PACHI
DOES IT STILL HURT, DARREN?
WELL, YEAH.
I'M FEELING MUCH BETTER THAN BEFORE, THOUGH.
AS IT HAPPENS...
...I AM THINKING OF STAYING HERE AT VAMPIRE MOUNTAIN AFTER THE COUNCIL, TO REPLACE SEBA AS THE QUARTERMASTER.
WHAT? QUARTER-MASTER?
SEBA OFFERED ME THE JOB.
HMM...
WELL, THE DESIRE IS WRITTEN PLAIN ON YOUR FACE.
YEARS AGO, IT WOULD HAVE BEEN THE FURTHEST THING FROM MY WISHES.
BUT LIFE HAS BEEN AIMLESS SINCE I QUIT THE GENERALS.
SOUNDS LIKE A GREAT PLAN. WHY NOT?
YOU THINK SO TOO?

I HAD NOT REALIZED HOW MUCH I MISSED BEING PART OF THE CLAN UNTIL I ATTENDED THIS COUNCIL.
THIS WOULD BE THE IDEAL WAY FOR ME TO REESTABLISH MYSELF.
BUT AS MY ASSISTANT, YOU WOULD HAVE TO REMAIN HERE FOR THE NEXT THIRTY YEARS...
...UNTIL YOU ARE OLD ENOUGH TO LEAVE BY YOURSELF.
I'VE ENJOYED MY STAY, BUT I IMAGINE IT COULD GROW BORING AFTER A COUPLE OF YEARS.
ヒョイ
HYOI (PLOP)
AND THERE'S HARKAT TO CONSIDER. HOW WILL HE GET BACK IF WE STAY HERE?
I WILL... STAY WITH YOU...IF YOU DECIDE...TO REMAIN.
YOU WILL?
PART OF...MY MEMORY... HAS COME BACK.
MUCH IS... STILL BLANK, BUT I...
...RECALL MR. TINY... TELLING ME THE ONLY... WAY I COULD ...
...FIND OUT WHO I...WAS BEFORE I DIED...
...WAS BY... STICKING WITH YOU.
HOW CAN I HELP YOU FIND OUT WHO YOU WERE?
I DO NOT... KNOW.
BUT I WILL... STAY BY YOUR... SIDE, AS LONG... AS YOU WILL... HAVE ME.
HARKAT HAD BEEN AT MY SIDE MORE THAN ANYONE ELSE THE PAST THREE DAYS.

IF I STAY HERE, I COULD LEARN MORE ABOUT THE WAYS OF THE VAMPIRES.
GORO (ROLL)
PERHAPS I COULD EVEN TRAIN ENOUGH TO BE A VAMPIRE GENERAL.
ON THE OTHER HAND, I'D MAYBE NEVER SEE MY FRIENDS AT THE CIRQUE DU FREAK AGAIN.
IT'S A HUGE DECISION.
CAN I HAVE SOME TIME TO THINK IT OVER?
OF COURSE. SEBA EXPECTS NO ANSWER UNTIL AFTER COUNCIL.
WE WILL DISCUSS IT AFTER YOU HAVE CONCLUDED YOUR TRIALS.
IF I CONCLUDE THEM.
NO, WHEN YOU DO.
TOMORROW IS THE FATEFUL DAY OF THE FOURTH TRIAL...
GOGOGOGO (RRMMBBMM)

CHAPTER 41:
ULTIMATE DESPERATION

I TRIED TO...FIX THE CLOTHES... THAT GOT RIPPED... ON THE PATH...OF NEEDLES.
WOW, HARKAT! THANKS A LOT!
WE LOOK ALIKE, DON'T WE?
THE STITCHING IS...NOT VERY GOOD...
NONSENSE! IT LOOKS GREAT, HEH HEH.
YOUR BURNS ARE...NOT HEALED FULLY. YOU STILL... MUST FIGHT?
YEAH.
I'LL GIVE IT MY BEST SHOT.
WAA (RAHHH)

...TAKING ONE CLEAN THROUGH HIS STOMACH, WHEREUPON IT REQUIRED REMOVAL AFTER THE TRIAL!
HE BRAVED A HAIL OF STALACTITES ON THE PATH OF NEEDLES...
OOO (OHHH)
THE LIVING HERO, HALF-VAMPIRE DARREN SHAN, SALLIES FORTH FOR HIS NEXT TRIAL!
IN THE HALL OF FLAMES, HE DEFTLY EVADED THE DRAUGHTS OF HELL...
IF YOU FAIL THIS TRIAL, THEY'LL MAKE OUT THAT YOU WERE A LAZY, STUPID, GOOD-FOR-NOTHING.
DON'T GO GETTING A SWOLLEN HEAD. EXAGGERATION IS THE KEY TO EVERY LEGEND.
DID YOU HEAR THAT? THEY'RE CALLING ME A HERO!
I'VE BROUGHT THE BEST WEAPONS I COULD FIND FOR YOU, DARREN. THEY'LL HAVE TO DO.
FUN (HMPH)
AT LEAST THEY WON'T BE ABLE TO SAY I SNORED LIKE A BEAR.
"WORK HARD, MY BOY," THEY'LL SAY TO FUTURE VAMPIRES, "OR YOU'LL END UP LIKE THAT WASTREL DARREN SHAN!"
YOU'VE BEEN SPENDING TOO MUCH TIME AROUND LARTEN!
BAN (WHAP)
OUCH!

JARA (CLANK)
ZUKI (WINCE)
THANKS A LOT, VANEZ.
THE FOURTH TRIAL IS UPON US.
ARE YOU PRE-PARED?
YES.
THEN BEGIN.
EVEN IN DEATH, MAY YOU BE TRIUM-PHANT.
ANIMALS THAT HAVE BEEN FED VAMPIRE BLOOD ARE GOING TO BE VICIOUS.
YOU'LL BE FINE. YOU ALREADY KILLED A BLOODED BEAR BEFORE.

THE FOURTH TRIAL OF INITIATION, THE BLOODED BOAR! NOW, BEGIN!!
WAAA (RAHHH)
THE PAIN IS STILL STABBING THROUGH ME, ESPECIALLY MY FEET.
I HAVE MOBILITY, BUT NOT MUCH. BETTER FINISH THIS ONE QUICKLY, OR ELSE...
HAA (CHUFF) HAA
GIVE ME YOUR BEST SHOT!
DON (BOOM)
GO (CRUNCH)

WAIT A SECOND ...
NOBODY SAID...
KA (STOMP)
...THERE WERE GOING TO BE TWO OF THEM!!

UH-OH...
I GET THE FEELING I FORGOT TO MENTION SOMETHING IMPORTANT...
GOKU (GULP)
GIRA (GLINT)
KNOCK 'EM OUT!
FIGHT!!
DO US PROUD, DARREN SHAN!!!
LOOK AT THE SIZE! THEY PROBABLY WEIGH MORE THAN THAT BEAR I FOUGHT
BUO (SNORT)
ZUDODO (DADUM DADUM)

TAKE THIS !!
DO (WHAM)
BOFUN (BFF)
IT'S NO GOOD JUST HACKING AWAY AT IT. YOU HAVE TO AIM FOR THE VITAL POINTS TO WIN.
BUFUU (SNORT)

DOSHAA (SLAM)
OOO (OOOH)
JIWA (BLOOM)
TH-THAT WAS CLOSE. HE COULD HAVE RIPPED A HUGE HOLE IN ME IF HE'D GOT NEARER!
IF I CAN'T HIT ANY VITAL SPOTS, THEN I'LL HAVE TO AIM FOR...!!
JIWA
GYA (GRAHH)
GUGU (HRRG)

WAA (RAHH)
DO (DMM)
DO
DO
BUGIII (SQUEEE)
WA (OOHH)

BU
(BSSHT)
DO
(RAHH)
BUSHI
(BLRRSHT)
GOA
(GRAHH)
DID THAT DO IT?
GURA
(FLOP)
FU
(ZZT)

ZUDOGOMU
(ZGROOM)
ZAWA
ZAWA
(MURMUR)
HEY, HE'S CAUGHT BETWEEN THE TWO!
IS HE OK!?
BON
(BOOM)
DAMN! I WASN'T THINKING ABOUT THE OTHER BOAR AT ALL!
GAHA
(GAHHK)
I'VE GOT TO GET AWAY!
WAIT, I CAN'T MOVE.
GU
GU
(TUG)
I'M TRAPPED UNDER THE BODY!
GOFU
(SNORT)

DO (DMM)
DO
DO
DO
DO
BA (LEAP)
DARREN!!
KUGU (KRRGG)
MOVE IT! GOT TO GET LOOSE!
I CAN'T DO IT! THERE IS NO ESCAPE!
IT'S THE END THIS TIME!
NO !!!!

GASP...
BIKI (RRMPH)
GOZU (GRRSHK)

DO
DO
DO
DO
DO
DO
DO
DO (DMM)
GA (SNAG)
PIKU (TWITCH)
FUWA (FLOAT)

ZUGA (THWAMM)
ZUZUUN (THUDD)
KEHO (COFF)
KEHO
GUI (TUG)
DARREN...
H... HARKAT...

NO... BROKEN BONES?
N-NONE.
......
......
COME... LET'S GO.
YOTA
YOTA (LIMP)

FOUL!!!

DIS-GRACE-FUL!!
BETRAYAL OF THE SACRED TRIALS!!
KILL THEM! PUT THEM BOTH TO DEATH!!
GOOOOO (BOOOOOO)

KILL THEM!!!
UMM... HAR-KAT?
EXECUTION!!
DEATH!!

PREPARE YOURSELF FOR THE CONSEQUENCES OF THIS ACTION, DARREN SHAN.

KILL THEM!!

KILL THEM!!

CHAPTER 42: LIFE OR DEATH?

I DOUBT YOU WILL ESCAPE A DEATH SENTENCE.

KILL THEM!!

KILL THEM!!

DON'T WORRY, DARREN. YOU'LL GET OUT OF THIS YET, I'M SURE OF IT.

THERE MUST BE A WAY.

Happy Birthday Darren Shan

CHAPTER 42: LIFE OR DEATH?

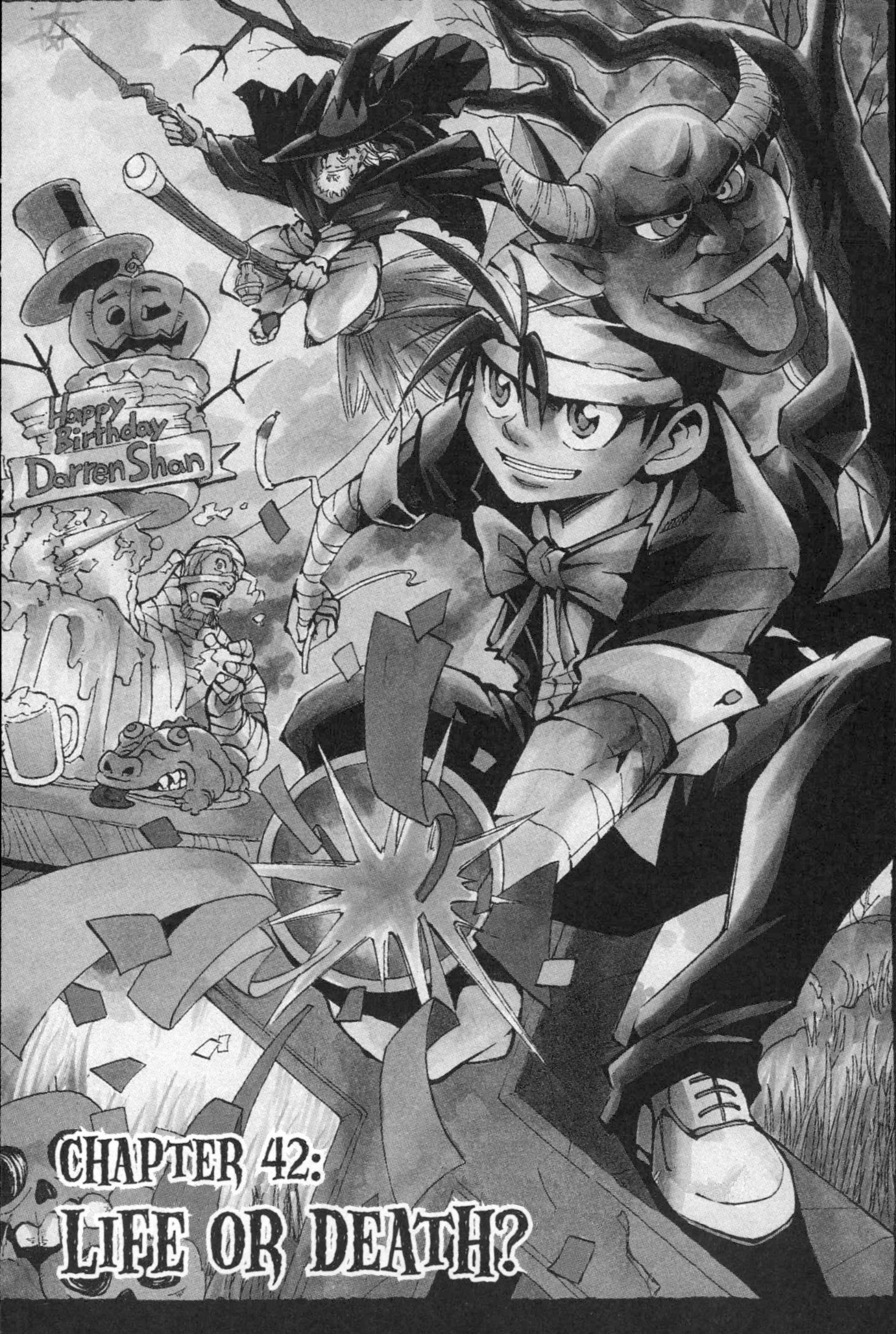

PACHI (POP)
PACHI
I DID NOT... MEAN TO... CAUSE TROUBLE ...
I ACTED... BEFORE I COULD... THINK.
I'D PROBABLY HAVE DONE THE SAME THING IF I WAS IN YOUR PLACE.
YOU ARE... NOT ANGRY?
OF COURSE NOT.
TO BE HONEST... I ACTED... FOR MY OWN SAKE...NOT YOURS.
IF YOU DIE, I MIGHT... NEVER FIND OUT... WHO I USED... TO BE.
MAYBE, BUT...
...THAT DOESN'T CHANGE THE FACT THAT YOU SAVED MY LIFE.
GORO (ROLL)
BURU (SHIVER)
BURU
KILL THEM!
KILL THEM!

SILENCE, MY BRETH-REN!!
ZA (ZSHH)
PEACE!!!
VANEZ ...
EVERY-ONE!
GII (CREAK)
SIRE!
THIS WAS NOT PLANNED! THE LITTLE PERSON DOESN'T KNOW OUR WAYS AND ACTED ON HIS OWN!
DON'T HOLD THIS AGAINST DARREN, I BEG YOU!

IS THIS TRUE, LITTLE PERSON?
DARREN MY...FRIEND. COULDN'T STAND BY... AND WATCH... HIM DIE.
A LIKELY STORY!
THEY HAVE CHEATED !!
SHIIIN (SHHH)
YOU HAVE DEFIED OUR RULES.
YOUR RULES. NOT MINE.
DARREN... FRIEND.
KILL THEM!
AN EXECU-TION!!
TAKE THEM BOTH TO THE HALL OF DEATH!
DARREN DIDN'T FAIL!
THE TRIAL WAS INTER-RUPTED!
DARREN PROVED HIS STRENGTH AND INGENUITY IN PREVIOUS TRIALS.
CAN ANYONE SAY FOR SURE THAT DARREN WOULD HAVE LOST?
KURDA IS RIGHT!
DOYO (JOSTLE)

HE HAD ALREADY MANAGED TO DEFEAT ONE OF THE BOARS!
I SAY DARREN HAS THE RIGHT TO RETAKE THE TRIAL!
IT'S ARRA ...
ARRA SAILS ...
... TAKING KURDA'S SIDE?
LARTEN? WHAT DO YOU SAY ABOUT THIS?
IT IS TRUE THAT DARREN WAS NOT ACTUALLY DEFEATED.
BUT WE CANNOT DENY THAT THE RULES HAVE BEEN BROKEN.
AND IN THE TRIALS, THERE ARE NO SECOND CHANCES.
LARTEN! YOU DON'T KNOW WHAT YOU'RE SAYING!
YES, HE DOES! AND HE'S RIGHT.
YORO CLURCH

I DON'T THINK I'D HAVE ESCAPED.
I DON'T WANT TO DIE, BUT I WON'T ASK FOR ANY SPECIAL FAVOURS.
IF IT'S POSSIBLE TO TAKE THE TRIAL AGAIN, I WILL.
IF NOT, I WON'T COMPLAIN.
KILL THEM!
EXE-CUTE HIM!
PUT THEM TO DEATH !!
VERY WELL. THERE WILL BE NO MEASURES TAKEN AGAINST HARKAT MULDS.
AS FOR YOUR FATE, I MUST SPEAK WITH MY FELLOW PRINCES AND GENERALS BEFORE PASSING SENTENCE.
MY ADVICE WOULD BE TO MAKE YOUR PEACE WITH THE GODS NOW.
RETURN TO YOUR CELL.
YOU'LL BE INFORMED OF OUR DECISION AS SOON AS WE REACH ONE.

KURDA SAID THAT HE HAD A PLAN UP HIS SLEEVE...
...BUT CAN I TRULY RELY ON THAT?
I PUT UP A BRAVE FRONT DOWN IN THE COLISEUM...
...BUT I'M SCARED STIFF INSIDE. I'M READY TO CRY AND BEG FOR MERCY.
NOT YOU... YOU'RE TOO... TOUGH.
I'VE DONE THIS BEFORE... I'VE SURVIVED SITUATIONS THAT I THOUGHT MEANT CERTAIN DEATH.
THERE'S NO REASON IT CAN'T HAPPEN AGAIN. I'M FINE...
I'LL MAKE IT...
EVERY MINUTE, EVERY SECOND HERE IS AGONY.
I CAN'T STAND THE WAITING.
DO (THUMP)
DO
I'M SCARED...
KA (TEK)
KA
HERE WE GO!
BA (CHOP)

PASA (FLAP)
WH-WHAT'S HAPPENING?
GAKU (SHIVER)
GAKU
D-DEATH ...
THEY'RE GOING TO DEMAND YOUR DEATH, DARREN.
FURA (SWOON)

I'VE TRIED ARGUING THEM OUT OF IT. GAVNER AND VANEZ PUT THEIR CAREERS ON THE LINE TO PLEAD FOR YOU.
BUT THERE AREN'T ANY PRECEDENTS. THE LAWS ARE CLEAR.
SO IT'S OVER.
I'M... FINISHED.
NO ...
NOT NECES-SARILY!
I DON'T UNDER-STAND. YOU JUST SAID...
CALM DOWN AND LISTEN, DARREN.

YOU CAN ESCAPE! YOU CAN GET OUT!
I KNOW A WAY PAST THE GUARDS!
I COULDN'T DO THAT!
MR. CREPSLEY WOULD BE ASHAMED OF ME!
YOU'RE NOT LARTEN'S RESPON-SIBILITY ANYMORE.
NOT SINCE YOU EM-BARKED ON THE TRIALS.
HE SPOKE COLDLY AND IMPASSIVE-LY ABOUT YOU IN THE COLISEUM...
...BUT HE IS BESEECH-ING THE PRINCES MORE THAN ANY OTHER.
NO ONE ELSE IS SEEKING A WAY FOR YOU TO LIVE HARDER THAN LARTEN.
T-T COULDN'T.
WHAT ABOUT YOU? IF THEY FOUND OUT YOU'D HELPED ME ESCAPE...
YOU'RE YOUNG, DARREN. IT'S CRAZY TO THROW YOUR LIFE AWAY.
PLEASE...
DON'T LET THE FOOLISH PRIDE OF OTHERS CLOUD YOUR JUDGMENT! BE YOUR OWN PERSON!

THE VAMPIRE SIDE OF ME IS SCREAMING TO ACCEPT MY FATE.
BUT THE OTHER SIDE—THE HUMAN SIDE—IS RESISTING.

NO ONE TRULY WANTS TO SEE YOU PUT TO DEATH, DARREN.
FOR MY SAKE, AND LARTEN'S...
...JUST RUN FOR YOUR LIFE!!

GYU (GRIP)
!
KOKU (NOD)
WELL DONE! WE MUST HURRY!
I WILL... COME.
SPEED IS OF THE ESSENCE IF WE ARE TO ESCAPE.
YOU WILL ONLY SLOW US DOWN. I'M AFRAID YOU MUST REMAIN HERE FOR NOW.

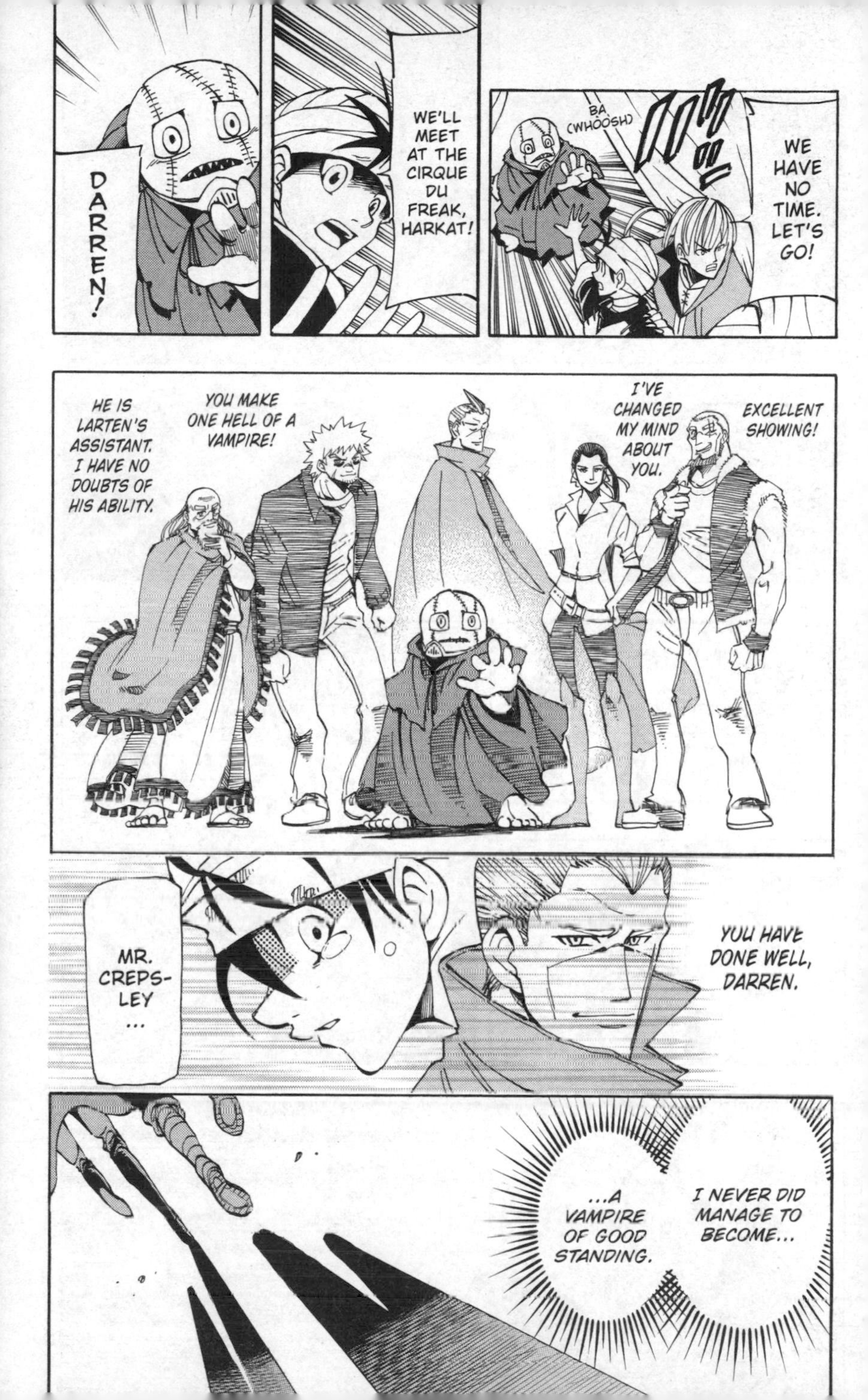
DARREN!
WE'LL MEET AT THE CIRQUE DU FREAK, HARKAT!
BA (WHOOSH)
WE HAVE NO TIME. LET'S GO!
EXCELLENT SHOWING!
I'VE CHANGED MY MIND ABOUT YOU.
YOU MAKE ONE HELL OF A VAMPIRE!
HE IS LARTEN'S ASSISTANT. I HAVE NO DOUBTS OF HIS ABILITY.
YOU HAVE DONE WELL, DARREN.
MR. CREPS-LEY ...
I NEVER DID MANAGE TO BECOME...
...A VAMPIRE OF GOOD STANDING.

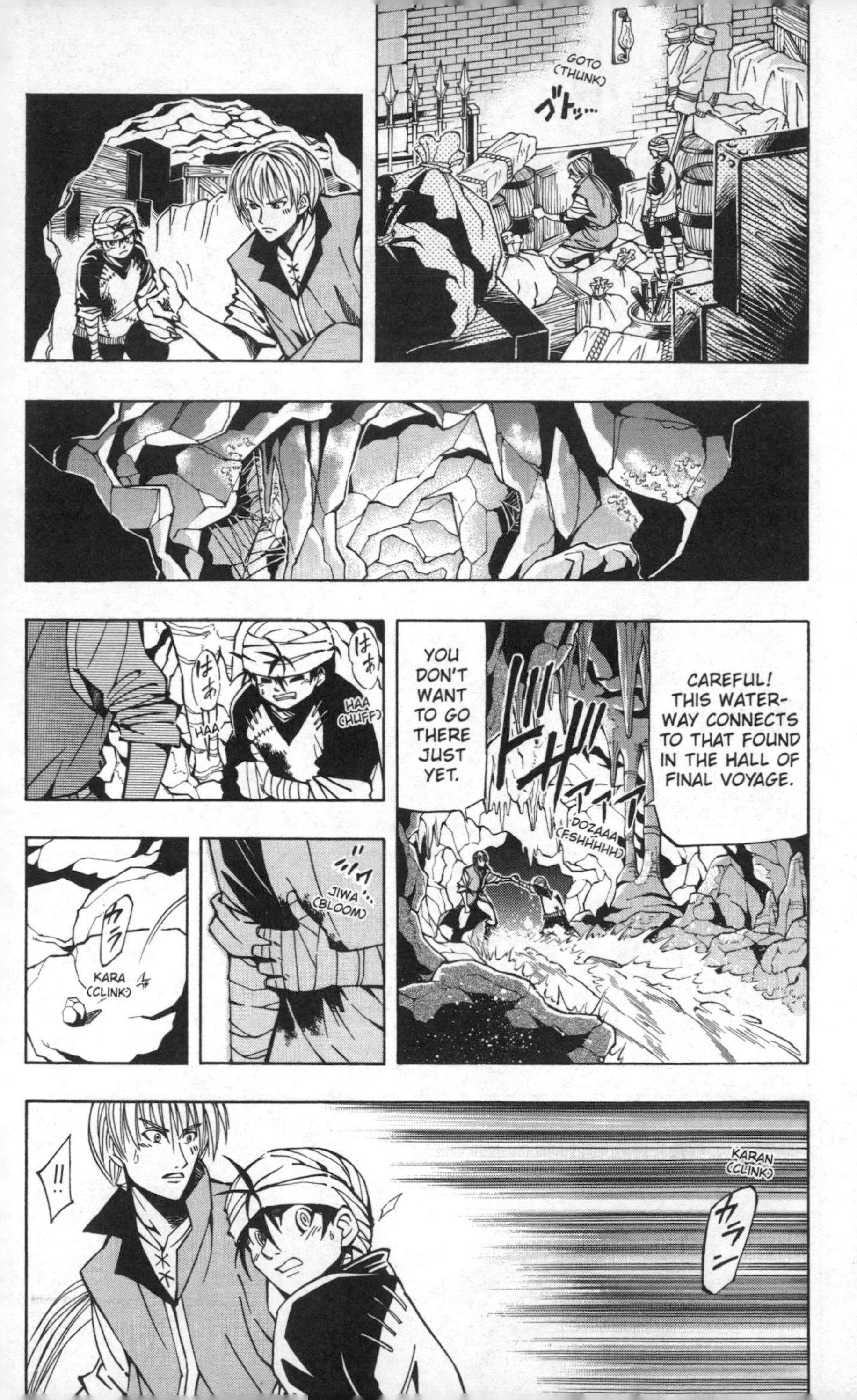
GOTO (THUNK)
ゴトッ…
はぁ
HAA (HUFF)
はぁ
HAA
CAREFUL! THIS WATER-WAY CONNECTS TO THAT FOUND IN THE HALL OF FINAL VOYAGE.
YOU DON'T WANT TO GO THERE JUST YET.
DOZAAA (F.SHHHHHH)
JIWA (BLOOM)
KARA (CLINK)
KARAN (CLINK)
!!

DADA (DASH)
HA
HA
PUR-SUERS ALREADY!?
I DON'T WANT TO BELIEVE IT, BUT I HEARD THE NOISE TOO!
RRGH!
DARREN!
WE CAN'T MAKE IT AWAY TOGETHER!
KEEP GOING, AND I CAN PRETEND THAT THIS WAS ALL MY IDEA!
NO, THAT'S RIDICULOUS!
JA (SCRAPE)
NU (HRMPH)

G-GAVNER! KURDA HAD NOTHING TO DO WITH THIS!
NO, DARREN !!
ZA (ZSHH)
BASHI (SMACK)
HOW DO YOU THINK I FELT, SEEING YOUR CELL EMPTY!?
YOU KNOW THAT ESCAPING DOESN'T SOLVE ANYTHING!
WHAT WAS I SUPPOSED TO TELL LARTEN!?
GAV-NER...
... ALLOW ME TO EXPLAIN.

VERY WELL. I SEE YOUR POINT, KURDA.
BUT YOU KNOW HOW FOOLISH IT WOULD BE TO DEFY THE PRINCES!
YES. BUT THERE ARE TIMES WHEN I AM HAPPY TO BE A FOOL. AND YOU ARE THE SAME.
IF YOU MEANT TO PUNISH US, YOU WOULDN'T HAVE COME ALONE.
YOU'RE RIGHT. I DON'T WANT TO SEE YOU KILLED.
I DON'T LIKE THIS ONE BIT, BUT IT SEEMS I HAVE NO CHOICE.
I'LL LET YOU GO...
...BUT ONLY ON ONE CONDITION.
ONCE YOU'RE A VAMPIRE PRINCE, YOU HAVE TO REVEAL THE TRUTH TO EVERYONE ELSE!
YOU MUST ABSOLVE DARREN OF HIS SHAME! SWEAR TO ME!
YOU HAVE MY WORD.
IF WE'RE GOING TO PULL THIS OFF, WE'D BETTER MOVE QUICKLY.
THERE'LL BE A TEAM OF TRACKERS ON DARREN'S TAIL SOON.

BUT BEFORE THAT, WE'LL WANT TO STOP YOUR BLEEDING, DARREN.
YOU MEAN... YOU FOLLOWED A BLOOD TRAIL?
NOT TO WORRY. I CLEANED UP ALL THE DROPS I FOUND.
VERY CARELESS OF YOU, KURDA.
INDEED...

LEFT AND RIGHT, UP AND DOWN WE WENT.
HOW MANY HOURS DID WE SPEND IN THOSE TUNNELS? AROUND ME I COULD HEAR THE ECHO OF RUNNING WATER.
GOOOO (WHOOOSHH)
I SEE! YES, I THINK YOU'D BE SAFE AT THE CIRQUE DU FREAK.
CAN I COME SEE YOU PERFORM, IF YOU GET OUT SAFELY?
YOU'LL HAVE TO TEACH ME HOW YOU CONTROL YOUR SPIDER.
SURE.
HA! I CAN'T WAIT!
WE'RE GOING TO TAKE A LEFT AT THIS FORK.
STICK CLOSE, YOU TWO.

WAIT...I'VE BEEN IN THIS PART OF THE MOUNTAIN BEFORE.
IT WAS DURING MY TRIALS OF INITIATION. I HAD TO FIND A HIDDEN JEWEL.

THE QUICKEST WAY TO THE OUT-SIDE IS ALONG THE RIGHT PATH!
GAV-NER, STOP!
TRUST ME. I KNOW WHERE I'M GOING.
WE'VE GOT TO FOLLOW THE MAPS. COME BACK!
WE PASSED THROUGH A SIDE-TUNNEL, THE ROARING SOUND OF NEARBY RUSHING WATER POUNDING OUR EARS.
GOOOOO (FW-SHHHH)
AT LAST, WE CAME TO ANOTHER CHAMBER.
SEE THAT? WE SAVED NEARLY FORTY MINUTES THIS WAY.
THIS WAS MY IDEA, GAVNER! ALLOW ME TO CALL THE SHOTS!
I DON'T DOUBT YOUR MAPS, BUT I'VE BEEN THROUGH THAT TUNNEL BEFORE. THERE'S NO NEED TO BE SO ANGRY...
GA (CRUNCH)
BE QUIET!!!
WHAT'S WRONG WITH YOU?
YOU'RE ACTING ODDLY.
......
NO, I'M NOT.
SORRY. THIS IS DARREN'S LIFE AT STAKE.
WHAT IF THAT SHORT-CUT HAD COLLAPSED?
I CHOSE THE ROUTE ON THE MAP THAT WOULD GIVE US THE SAFEST MEANS OF ESCAPE!

RIGHT. OF COURSE.
I'VE JUST BEEN SCOLDED!
HOWEVER, IT'S TRUE THAT YOU HAVE SPED OUR PROGRESS. LET'S CONTINUE ...
AGREED.
JA (SCRAPE)
ジャ…
GOHO (KOFF)
ゴホッ
DID YOU JUST HEAR THAT, DARREN?
SOUNDED LIKE A COUGH.
HUH?
WHAT IS GOING ON?
WE DON'T HAVE ALL THE TIME IN THE WORLD.
SOME-ONE ON OUR TRAIL?
NO— IT WOULD HAVE COME FROM BEHIND. THEY CAN'T POSSIBLY HAVE CIRCLED AHEAD.
BUT IT CLEARLY CAME FROM OVER HERE...
COME, GAVNER!
DON'T WORRY, I'M JUST CHECKING!
WE'LL LEAVE ONCE I'VE MADE SURE WE'RE SAFE.

YURA (SWISH)
WHAT IS IT?
PEOPLE? ABOUT TWENTY TO THIRTY, LOOKS LIKE...
GUARDIANS OF THE BLOOD? NO, THEY'RE TOO BIG.
THEY'RE VAMPIRES. BUT WHY ...?
GAVNER!?
BUT I KNEW WHAT THEY REALLY WERE.
IT WAS IMPOSSIBLE.
I COULD NOT BELIEVE MY OWN EYES.
RED HAIR, CRIMSON EYES, PURPLE SKIN...
YES. I KNEW WHO THEY WERE.

VAMPANEZE!!!

CHAPTER 43:
AN UNEXPECTED
TURN OF EVENTS

THOSE ARE VAMPANEZE, ALL RIGHT.
ARE YOU TWO SATISFIED?
IT WAS YOUR IMAGINATION.
MY GOODNESS!
SHH!
QUIET...
LET'S BACK AWAY.
ARE THEY HERE TO ATTACK US?
THEY MIGHT HAVE COME TO DISCUSS A TREATY.

YOU THINK SO?
NO...
...NOT REALLY.
WE HAVE TO WARN THE VAMPIRES.
LET'S GO BACK.
BUT WHAT ABOUT YOUR ESCAPE?
ONE OF US CAN LEAD YOU TO—
FORGET IT, I'M NOT RUNNING AWAY FROM SOMETHING LIKE THIS.
WE'VE GOT TO TELL MR. CREPSLEY AND THE PRINCES ABOUT IT!
DARREN...
LISTEN, THIS IS WHERE WE ARE NOW.
THERE'S A THREE-WAY SPLIT UP AHEAD, AND THE MIDDLE PATH WILL TAKE US BACK TO THE HALLS...
...BUT IT'LL TAKE A LONG TIME, AND WE'LL PASS VERY CLOSE TO THAT CAVE THE VAMPANEZE WERE IN.

LET'S GO!
HOP BACK ON, DARREN.
HONESTLY, THIS INJURY IS NOTHING.
THANKS FOR CARRYING ME THIS FAR, GAVNER, BUT I'M FINE ON MY OWN NOW.
NOW THAT'S A LITTLE MORE LIKE IT!
NIYA (SMIRK)
DA DA (DMM)
SFX: JA (SCRAPE)
WHA ...?
HOW CAN THIS BE? THE TUNNEL HAS COLLAPSED ...
DAMN! WHY NOW, OF ALL TIMES!?

I'M SORRY... WE'LL HAVE TO RETURN AND TAKE THE MIDDLE PATH.
IT'S POSSIBLE THAT THE VAMPANEZE MAY HAVE MOVED FROM THEIR POSITION. WE'LL HAVE TO TAKE THE SURE ROUTE.
PON (PAT)
IT'S NOT YOUR FAULT. YOU COULDN'T HAVE KNOWN.
IF THEY SPOT US, FIGHT FOR YOUR LIVES—THEN RUN LIKE HELL!
WAIT! I DON'T HAVE A WEAPON.
I ONLY HAVE ONE KNIFE.
GAVNER?
I HAVE TWO.
GREAT, I CAN USE ONE!
SORRY, DARREN. I'LL NEED BOTH OF THEM TO FIGHT.
SHU (SWISH)
SHUKA (SHHIK)
SO WHAT WILL I FIGHT WITH?
BAD BREATH!!?

HA-HA-HA! YOU DO THAT, DARREN.
IF KURDA AND I CAN'T FEND THEM OFF, I DON'T THINK YOU'LL MAKE MUCH OF A DIFFERENCE, WEAPON OR NOT.
I'M SERIOUS! I CAN FIGHT!
I FIRST MET YOU AT THE CIRQUE DU FREAK, WHAT...SIX YEARS AGO, WAS IT?
AT THE TIME, I THOUGHT YOU WERE JUST SOME SNOT-NOSED KID...
...BUT YOU'VE GOT A MORE IMPORTANT ROLE THAN FIGHTING NOW.
TO TELL THE PRINCES ABOUT THE VAMPANEZE !!
GUSHA (SCRUNCH)
BUT —!
TRY TO UNDER-STAND HIS POINT OF VIEW, DARREN.

WE STAYED SILENT, MOVING TOO SLOWLY TO RAISE ECHOING FOOT-STEPS.
OCCASION-ALLY WE STOPPED TO REST, STRAINING OUR EARS FOR PUR-SUERS.
EVENTUALLY I HEARD VOICES, TALKING QUIETLY, LAUGHING RAUCOUSLY.
HA HA HA HA
BWA
HEE HEE HEE HEE HEE
APPARENTLY WE WERE REACHING THE EARLIER VAMPANEZE OUTPOST.
JUST BEYOND THIS WALL IS A THRONG OF VAMPANEZE.
IF I WASN'T WITH THESE TWO NOBLE WARRIORS, I'D BE GOING CRAZY WITH FEAR.
!!
WAIT! IS THERE A HIDING SPOT?
DAMN!
GUI (SHRUG)
WHEWWWW...
I CAN'T TAKE THIS AC-CURSED CHILL...

BA
(ZWWP)
JA
(SCRAPE)
GOTO
(THUD)
SORRY, PAL. WE'RE TRYIN' TO STAY HIDDEN BACK HERE.

DO (STOMP)
UOO (RAHHH)
DO
DO
SO MUCH FOR STEALTH.
VAMPIRES!!!
YOU TWO GET OUT OF HERE. I'LL DELAY THEM AS LONG AS I CAN.
I WON'T LEAVE YOU TO FACE THEM ALONE!
YOU WILL IF YOU HAVE ANY BRAINS!!
THIS TUNNEL'S NARROW. ONE PERSON CAN HOLD THEM OFF! TAKE VARREN AND BREAK FOR THE HALLS!
BUT —!
YOU'RE ARGUING OUR CHANCES AWAY!
DOSHU (USHHH)

COME, DARREN!
NO, I WANT TO STAY WITH GAVNER!!
ZORO (LOOM)
ZORO
LET ME GO, KURDA!! LET GO!!
IF WE FOLLOW THIS TUNNEL STRAIGHT, IT WILL LEAD TO THAT BURIAL CHAMBER, THE HALL OF FINAL VOYAGE!
WAIT THERE FOR GAVNER OR ME TO CATCH UP. IF NOBODY COMES, MAKE YOUR WAY BACK TO THE HALLS ALONE!
WHAT ARE YOU GOING TO DO?
I'M GOING...
...TO HELP GAVNER.
TWO OF US WORKING TOGETHER STAND A BETTER CHANCE OF HOLDING THEM!
LEAVE IMMEDIATELY, DARREN! DON'T WAIT AROUND!

WAIT FOR US AT THE HALL OF FINAL VOYAGE!
GOT THAT!?
......
DOSHA (THWAM)
WHAT, IS THAT ALL?
ZE (WHEEZE)
ZE
I THOUGHT YOU VAMPANEZE WERE TOUGHER.
GRR...
SFX: ZUN (STOMP) ZUN
MOVE. I WILL FIGHT.
THE LEADER, EH?
NI (GRIN)

WHAT... SHOULD I DO?
OBVIOUSLY, FOLLOWING KURDA'S PLAN IS THE BEST IDEA.
I UNDER-STAND HIS REASONS ...
...BUT I CAN'T LEAVE MY FRIEND BEHIND TO DIE WITHOUT EVEN RAISING A HAND TO HELP HIM!
HE'S ONLY IN THIS SITUATION BECAUSE HE TRIED TO HELP ME!
KURDA'S A POTENTIAL CANDIDATE FOR PRINCE! HE'S TOO IMPORTANT TO BE HURT!
IT SHOULD HAVE BEEN ME WHO STAYED BEHIND TO HELP GAVNER!
I CAN STILL MAKE IT! I JUST HAVE TO CATCH UP TO KURDA!
GIIN (CLANGG)
ZEE (WHEEZE)
ZEE
HAA (CHUFF)
HAA
GAVNER!!

KURDA! WHY?
I TOLD YOU TO LEAVE! WHAT ABOUT DARREN?
I GAVE HIM DIRECTIONS TO GET BACK.
YOU'RE A FOOL, KURDA.
I KNOW.
A GREAT BIG FOOL.
PLEASE LET ME MAKE IT IN TIME!
BE CAREFUL, THIS ONE'S TOUGH.
I HATE TO BE COWARDLY, BUT WE NEED TWO-ON-ONE HERE!
OH GOOD! THEY'RE BOTH STILL ALIVE!

RAAAAHH!!
DA (DASH)
GAKI (KCHANGG)
BUOO (VWOOM)
NOW, KURDA !!
KURDA!!
GAVNER!!!

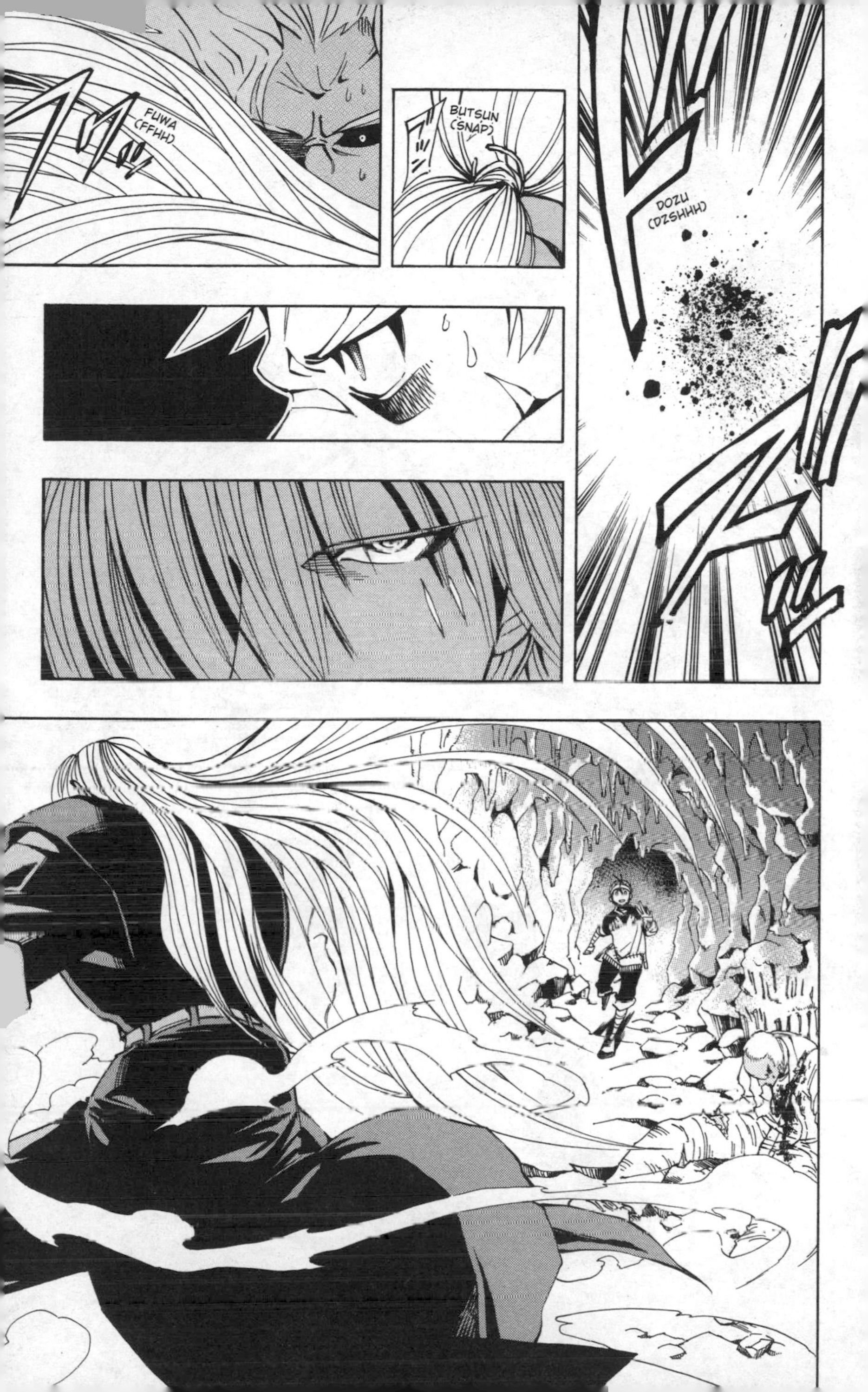
DOZU
(DZSHHH)
BUTSUN
(SNAP)
FUWA
(FFHH)

GUGU (TUG)
HEH.
HEH HEH.
ZUZUZU (SLIDE)
HUH...?

GAVNER, COLLAPSING.

KURDA, WATCHING IMPASSIVELY.

CHAPTER 44: EVEN IN DEATH

I COULDN'T UNDERSTAND WHAT WAS HAPPENING.
HOW COULD THIS BE? WHY?
MY EYES TOLD ME EVERYTHING. IT WAS NOT A VAMPANEZE WHO STABBED GAVNER.

NO, THE ONE WHO STABBED HIM...
...WHO PLUNGED HIS KNIFE DEEP INTO GAVNER'S SIDE WAS...
... KURDA SMAHLT.

CHAPTER 44:
EVEN IN DEATH

I THOUGHT FOR A MINUTE YOU WERE COMING TO HIS AID.
NO ...
I'D HAVE KNOCKED HIM OUT AND TAKEN HIM AWAY SOME-WHERE IF POSSIBLE...
...BUT OTHERS COULD HAVE TRACKED DOWN HIS MENTAL SIGNALS.
THERE'S A BOY UP AHEAD, A HALF-VAMPIRE.
HE'S INJURED, SO HE WON'T BE HARD TO CATCH.
I WANT HIM TAKEN ALIVE. THEY WON'T BE ABLE TO TRACK HIM WITH THE STONE OF BLOOD.
DO YOU MEAN THE BOY BEHIND YOU?
WHAT !!?

YORO (SLUMP)
DARREN! HOW LONG HAVE YOU BEEN THERE?
ZEE ZEE (WHEEZE)
GAVNER! OH...
DARREN!
GOHO (KOFF)
GAHA (GACK)
DOKU
DOKU (BADUM)

HE CAN'T ...
...SEE ME...
ニチャ
NICHA (SLRCH)
I KNOW THIS FEELING ...
TOKUN (THUMP)
TOKUN
THE FEELING OF THE SPARK OF LIFE...
... SLOWLY BUT SURELY SLIPPING THROUGH MY FINGERS ...
I'M WITH YOU, CAVNER.
YOU'RE NOT ALONE. I'LL...
SUH...
SUH...
WHAT IS IT?
SPEAK, GAV-NER!

S-
SORRY
...
...IF
M-M-MY
SNORING
...
...
K-KEPT
YOU...
AWAKE
...

UWAAAAAAH!
AAAAH!
HIKKU (HIC)
HIKKU
YOU KILLED HIM! YOU KILLED GAVNER!!
GOKU (GULP)
I HAD TO, DARREN.

THERE WAS NO TIME TO LET HIM DIE A NOBLE DEATH.
YOU MIGHT HAVE GOT AWAY IF I'D LEFT HIM FOR THE VAMPANEZE.
YOU KNEW THEY WERE HERE ALL ALONG!
YOU'RE IN LEAGUE WITH THE VAMPANEZE!
YES...
THAT'S WHY I DIDN'T WANT TO TAKE THE ROUTE UNDER THE STREAM.
I FEARED THIS WOULD HAPPEN.
EVERYTHING WOULD HAVE BEEN FINE IF WE'D GONE THE WAY I WANTED.
I'M TRYING TO SAVE OUR RACE, NOT CONDEMN IT.
GAVNER'S DEATH IS REGRET-TABLE, BUT WHEN I EXPLAIN PROP—
TO HELL WITH YOUR EXPLANA-TIONS!!
PLEASE, KURDA... TELL ME THIS IS ALL A MISTAKE...
YOU DON'T UNDER-STAND WHAT'S HAPPEN-ING.
THERE ARE THINGS YOU DON'T KNOW— THINGS NO VAMPIRE KNOWS.

YOU'RE A TRAITOR AND A MURDERER—SCUM!
DARREN...
STAY BACK!
GA (SNATCH)
NO! I SAID I WANTED HIM TAKEN ALIVE!
HE HAS A WEAPON.
DO YOU WANT US TO LET HIM CHOP OFF OUR FINGERS AS WE PRY IT AWAY?
STOP, KURDA! DON'T COME ANY CLOSER ...!!
I'M UNARMED.
DON'T WORRY, GLALDA.
I'M IN CONTROL OF THE SITUATION.

I DON'T CARE. I'LL KILL YOU ANYWAY.
YOU DESERVE IT.
MAYBE SO...
...BUT I DON'T THINK YOU'D KILL AN UNARMED MAN, NO MATTER WHAT HE'D DONE.
IF I'M WRONG, I'LL PAY FOR MY ERROR OF JUDGEMENT...
...IN THE SEVEREST WAY POSSIBLE...
JA (SCRAPE)
...BUT...
KATA
KATA (SHIVER)
ZA (STEP)
ZA
...I DON'T THINK I AM.
I HATE YOU!!
KA (KKOW)
HE'S GET-TING AWAY!!
WAIT! HE'S GOT A WEAPON! WE'LL HAVE TO WEAKEN HIM BEFORE WE TAKE HIM!
COVER ALL THE PASSAGE-WAYS THAT LEAD UP TO THE HALLS!
DON'T KILL HIM, UNDER ANY CIRCUM-STANCES!

SHU (SWISH)
I'LL NEED BOTH OF THEM TO FIGHT.
GUSHA (SCRUNCH)
YOU'VE GOT A MORE IMPORTANT ROLE THAN FIGHTING NOW.

GAVNER!

ZA (STOMP)
ZA
ZA

REMEMBER KURDA'S MAP.
IF I FOLLOW THIS PATH, IT SHOULD TAKE ME TO THE HALL OF FINAL VOYAGE!

I'VE GOT TO REACH THE OTHERS...
...EVEN IF IT MEANS LOSING MY LEGS!
BUSH (BSHH)

HAA (HUFF)
HAA
GOOOOOOO (SHWFFFFF)
FURA (SWOON)
GARA (CLANK)
GASHA (CLANK)
WHERE IS THE BOY?
UP AHEAD!
WHICH EXIT LEADS TO THE HALLS?
DAMN, IT'S THE ONE ACROSS FROM THE WATER!
WAIT, WHAT'S THAT!?
A GUARDIAN OF THE BLOOD!
ORO (GAPE)
ORO
HELP! VAMPANEZE HAVE INVADED!
YOU'VE GOT TO WARN THE GENERALS!

HEY!
TA (TEK) TA
THERE HE IS! GET HIM!
DA (DASH)
NO! WAIT!
THE EXIT'S ON THE OTHER SIDE OF THE STREAM. CAN I JUMP IT?
I HAVE TO! IF I DON'T, MR. CREPSLEY AND HARKAT ...
...ALL MY FRIENDS ...
...WILL BE IN DANGER!
REACH THE FAR BANK!
REACH!

DOPPAN (KABLOOSHH)
PUHA (GASP)
GA (SNAG)

NO! HIS DEATH SERVES NO PURPOSE.
HE'S YOUNG AND OPEN TO NEW IDEAS.
SOME-BODY GRAB ME AND LOWER ME DOWN.
WHY? LET HIM DROWN.
IT'LL BE EASIER.
WE'LL NEED VAMPIRES LIKE HIM IF WE'RE GOING TO—
OKAY, OKAY.
DODODODODODODO (FWWOOOSHHHH)
REACH OUT YOUR HAND, DARREN. THERE'S NO USE IN BEING STUBBORN HERE.
YOUR DEATH WOULD BE MEANING-LESS. LET ME SAVE YOU.
WHY DID YOU DO IT?
I DON'T WANT TO LOSE YOU, DARREN.
THE VAMPANEZE WON'T HARM YOU...I PROMISE.
IT'S TOO COMPLI-CATED.
COME WITH ME AND I'LL EXPLAIN LATER.

YOU PROMISE...?
YOU'RE A LIAR AND A TRAITOR.
I WOULDN'T BELIEVE YOU IF YOU SAID THE WORLD WAS ROUND.
BELIEVE WHAT YOU WANT...
...BUT I'M ALL THAT STANDS BETWEEN YOU AND A WATERY GRAVE.
I KNOW YOU, DARREN. YOU DON'T WANT TO DIE.
THINK OF ALL THE TIMES I'VE SAVED YOUR LIFE.
I THOUGHT THE SAME WAY...
BA (WHOOSH)
UOOO (RAHHH)
I THOUGHT YOU WERE SOMEONE WHO WOULD CARE FOR ME AND UNDER-STAND ME.
I THOUGHT OF YOU LIKE AN OLDER BROTHER!
I TRUSTED YOU!!
YOU DON'T KNOW A THING ABOUT HONOUR OR LOYALTY.
IF BEING SAVED MEANS GIVING MYSELF UP TO SCUM LIKE YOU...
PA (SLIP)
DARREN, NO!
...THEN I CHOOSE DEATH.

GO!!
(SWSHH)
EVEN IN DEATH ...
...MAY I BE TRIUMPHANT !!!
IN THIS VERY MOMENT, AS I STARED DEATH IN THE FACE...
...I FELT A STRANGE MOMENT OF PEACE.
DO (FSHHH)
DO (FSHHH)
I COULD SEE KURDA SHOUTING SOMETHING...
...BUT HIS WORDS WERE LOST BEFORE THEY REACHED MY EARS.

VAMPIRE GODS, WELCOME ME INTO YOUR ARMS!
SMILE UPON MY DEATH AND EXACT A TERRIBLE REVENGE AGAINST THE TRAITOR KURDA AND HIS ALLIES!

ALL SOUND AND LIGHT VANISHED ...
...AS I WAS SUCKED INTO DARKNESS, CHURNING MADNESS ...
... AND I PLUNGED, DEEPER AND DEEPER ...
...INTO THE HUNGRY BELLY OF VAMPIRE MOUNTAIN.
TRIALS OF DEATH - END

GAVNERRR!!
A QUICK GUIDE TO THE STORY OF THE CIRQUE DU FREAK MANGA VERSION
(SORT OF)!!
PART 5!!!!!
I SAT DOWN TO READ VOLUME 5 OF THE CIRQUE DU FREAK NOVELS, "TRIALS OF DEATH."
IT WAS A LOVELY, SUNNY, SPRING DAY.
WAKU WAKU (AHHH)
I'M GOING TO READ VOLUME 5 TODAY!
CAN'T WAIT TO FIND OUT WHAT HAPPENS IN DARREN'S TRIALS!
AS I READ...
GRR...
COME ON, DARREN! PASS THOSE TRIALS!
PERA (FLIP)
PERA
WHAT? HE'S ESCAPING?
PERA
THE VAMPANEZE ARE HERE?
PERA
PERA
PERA
PERA
PERA
PERA
PERA
PERA
PERA
PERA
PERA
WHAT!? WHAT'S GOING ON!?
HANG IN THERE, GAVNER!!
PERARI (FLIP)
EXCELLENT! GOOD TIMING, KURDA!!

PERA
ペラ…
!!
!?
BOOK: CIRQUE DU FREAK 5
AAAAGHHH!!!
...
I TOLD YOU TO SHUT...
BUT...LOOK! GAVNER! OH NO!
SFX: SHA (SHKK)
GAVNER'S DEAD!!
OH, GAVNER!! POOR GAVNER!!
OH, SHUT UP...
...UP!!!!!!
GASU (STAB)
GYEE!!
MUKURI (RISE)
OH, THE HUMANITY!!

IT WAS THAT SHOCKING TO ME.
MUM, THERE'S A BIG DEAD FROG OVER THERE!
WELL, DON'T STARE AT IT.
I HATE FROGS...
BYON (BOING)
BYON
FIRST SAM, NOW GAVNER—ALL OF MY FAVOURITE CHARACTERS SEEM TO DIE OFF JUST WHEN I'M GETTING USED TO DRAWING THEM.
IT'S NOT FAIR, DARREN-SAN...
JUST AS THE NUMBER OF PAGES IN A SERIES OF NOVELS CHANGES EVERY BOOK, SO DOES THE COMPLEXITY OF THE STORY.
SINCE THE NUMBER OF PAGES FOR THE MANGA IS THE SAME EVERY TIME, THE DIFFICULTY IN TURNING IT INTO A COMIC WILL VARY.
THE FIFTH VOLUME WAS ESPECIALLY HARD FOR ME.
ARRRGH!
I CAN'T WRAP UP AN ENTIRE TRIAL IN JUST EIGHTEEN PAGES!!
SFX: KUSHA (CRUMPLE) KUSHA
THIS IS SUCH A WASTE! WHY DO I HAVE TO PACK AN ENTIRE NOVEL INTO JUST A SINGLE VOLUME OF MANGA!?
I SHOULD BE ALLOWED TO SPREAD VOLUME 5 OVER TWO BOOKS!!
GARI
GARI
GARI
IN THAT CASE, YOU CAN STOP WORKING ON IT.
GASHAKON (KA-CHUNK)
GARI
GARI (SCRATCH)

THAT'S A BIT MORE LIKE IT.
I'M SORRY, MASTER!
NOT ONLY WERE THE TRIALS RUSHED...
GASHIN (PRANCE)
GASHIN
...BUT I WOULD HAVE LIKED TO SPEND MORE TIME ON THE FESTIVAL OF THE UNDEAD.
IF YOU WANT TO KNOW THE STORY BEHIND GAVNER'S UNDERWEAR, CHECK OUT "AN AFFAIR OF THE NIGHT" ON DARREN SHAN'S WEBSITE.
YOU'LL CRY YOUR EYES OUT!
CIRQUE THE MANGA HAS REACHED FIVE VOLUMES NOW. THAT'S AN ENTIRE YEAR'S WORTH OF WEEKLY CHAPTERS.
JIWA (SNIFF)
IT BRINGS A TEAR TO MY EYE TO SEE THEM ALL LINED UP IN THE BOOKSHOP.
I'VE NEVER HAD A MORE FULL AND REWARDING YEAR IN MY LIFE.
AND IT WAS ONLY POSSIBLE WITH THE HELP OF ALL THE FAITHFUL READERS. THANK YOU ALL!
THE "VAMPIRE MOUNTAIN SAGA" IS ABOUT TO REACH ITS CLIMAX!
WILL DARREN LIVE OR DIE? WHAT IS KURDA'S TRUE GOAL? FIND OUT ALL THE ANSWERS IN VOLUME 6!

BOOKS: CIRQUE 1, CIRQUE 2, CIRQUE 3, CIRQUE 4

The End

THE SAGA OF DARREN SHAN ⑤
Trials of Death

Darren Shan
Takahiro Arai

Translation: Stephen Paul
Lettering: AndWorld Design
Art direction: Hitoshi SHIRAYAMA
Original cover design: Shigeru ANZAI + Bay Bridge Studio

Darren Shan Vol. 5

Original Japanese edition published in Japan in 2007
by Shogakukan Inc., Tokyo
Artwork reproduction rights in U.K. and The Commonwealth arranged
with Shogakukan Inc. through Tuttle-Mori Agency, Inc., Tokyo.

Published in Great Britain by Harper Collins *Children's Books* 2010
Harper Collins *Children's Books* is a division of HarperCollins *Publishers* Ltd
77-85 Fulham Palace Road, Hammersmith, London, W6 8JB

www.harpercollins.co.uk

ISBN: 978 0 00 733272 4

Printed and bound in Great Britain by Clays Ltd, St Ives plc

DARREN SHAN
VAMPIRE MOUNTAIN

THE SAGA OF DARREN SHAN
BOOK 4

Darren Shan and Mr Crepsley embark on a dangerous trek to the very heart of the vampire world. But they face more than the cold on Vampire Mountain – the vampaneeze have been there before them...

Will a meeting with the Vampire Princes restore Darren's human side, or turn him further towards the darkness? Only one thing is certain – Darren's initiation into the vampire clan is more deadly than he can ever have imagined.

ISBN 978 0 00 711441 2

DARREN SHAN
TUNNELS OF BLOOD

THE SAGA OF DARREN SHAN
BOOK 3

Darren Shan, the Vampire's Assistant, gets a taste of city life when he leaves the Cirque Du Freak with Evra and Mr Crepsley. At night the vampire goes about secret business, while by day Darren enjoys his freedom.

But then bodies are discovered... Corpses drained of blood... The hunt for the killer is on and Darren's loyalties are tested to the limit as he fears the worst. One mistake and they are all doomed to perish in the tunnels of blood...

Also available on audio, read by Rupert Degas

PB ISBN 978 0 00 675541 2
CD ISBN 978 0 00 721419 8

DARREN SHAN

THE VAMPIRE'S ASSISTANT

THE SAGA OF DARREN SHAN
BOOK 2

Darren Shan was just an ordinary schoolboy – until his visit to the Cirque Du Freak. Now, as he struggles with his new life as a Vampire's Assistant, he tries desperately to resist the one thing that can keep him alive... blood. But a gruesome encounter with the Wolf Man may change all that...

Also available on audio, read by Rupert Degas

PB ISBN 978 0 00 675513 5
CD ISBN 978 0 00 721417 4

DARREN SHAN

CIRQUE DU FREAK

THE SAGA OF DARREN SHAN
BOOK 1

Darren Shan is just an ordinary schoolboy – until he gets an invitation to visit the Cirque Du Freak... until he meets Madam Octa... until he comes face to face with a creature of the night.

Soon, Darren and his friend Steve are caught in a deadly trap. Darren must make a bargain with the one person who can save Steve. But that person is not human and only deals in blood...

Also available on audio, read by Rupert Degas

PB ISBN 978 0 00 675416 9
CD ISBN 978 0 00 721415 0

DARREN SHAN
BEC

BOOK FOUR OF THE DEMONATA

As a baby, Bec fought for her life. As a trainee priestess, she fights to fit in to a tribe that needs her skills but fears her powers. And when the demons come, the fight becomes a war.

Bec's magic is weak and untrained, until she meets the druid Drust. Under his leadership, Bec and a small band of warriors embark on a long journey through hostile lands to confront the Demonata at their source. But the final conflict demands a sacrifice too horrific to contemplate...

Also available on audio, read by Lorraine Pilkington

PB ISBN 978 0 00 723139 3
CD ISBN 978 0 00 722979 6

DARREN SHAN
SLAWTER

BOOK THREE OF THE DEMONATA

Nightmares haunt the dreams of Dervish Grady since his return from the Demonata universe, but Grubbs takes care of his uncle as they both try to continue a normal, demon-free existence. When a legendary cult director calls in Dervish as consultant for a new horror movie, it seems a perfect excuse for a break from routine and a chance for some fun. But being on the set of a town called Slawter stirs up more than memories for Grubbs and his friend Bill-E.

Also available on audio, read by Rupert Degas

PB ISBN 978 0 00 723138 6
CD ISBN 978 0 00 722978 9

DARREN SHAN
DEMON THIEF

BOOK TWO OF **THE DEMONATA**

When Kernel Fleck's brother is stolen by demons, he must enter their universe in search of him. It is a place of magic, chaos and incredible danger. Kernel has three aims:

- learn to use magic,
- find his brother,
- stay alive.

But a heartless demon awaits him, and death has been foretold…

Also available on audio, read by Rupert Degas

PB ISBN 978 0 00 719323 3
CD ISBN 978 0 00 722977 2

DARREN SHAN
LORD LOSS

BOOK ONE OF **THE DEMONATA**

When Grubbs Grady first encounters Lord Loss and his evil minions, he learns three things:

- the world is vicious,
- magic is possible,
- demons are real.

He thinks that he will never again witness such a terrible night of death and darkness.

…He is wrong.

Also available on audio, read by Rupert Degas

PB ISBN 978 0 00 719320 2
CD ISBN 978 0 00 721389 4

Vampires | Demons
Contact
Shanville Monthly
Blog
Facts
Photos
Links
Messageboard
Extras
Vampires
Demons
Darren Shan
.com

THE SAGA OF DARREN SHAN

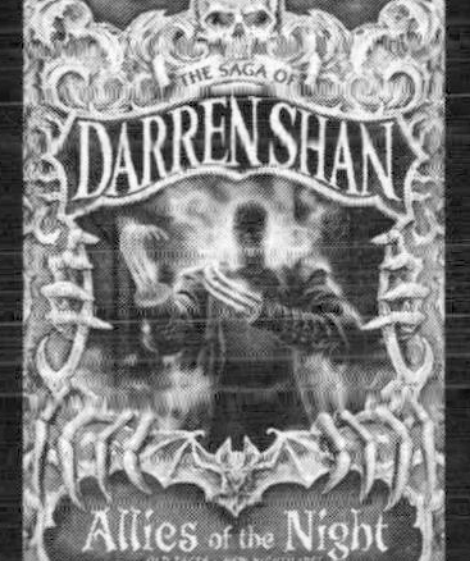

THE DEMONATA
DARREN SHAN
Lord Loss
IT'S IN THE BLOOD...
DARREN SHAN
Demon Thief
GO TO HELL...
DARREN SHAN
NUMBER ONE MASTER OF HORROR
Slawter
THE DIRECTOR'S CUT IS FATAL...
DARREN SHAN
NUMBER ONE MASTER OF HORROR
BEC
SCREAMS IN THE DARK...
DARREN SHAN
NUMBER ONE MASTER OF HORROR
Blood Beast
UNLEASH THE MONSTER...
DARREN SHAN
NUMBER ONE MASTER OF HORROR
Demon Apocalypse
HELL IS REVEALED...
DARREN SHAN
NUMBER ONE MASTER OF HORROR
Death's Shadow
YOU CAN'T CHEAT DEATH...
DARREN SHAN
WOLF ISLAND
TRESPASSERS WILL BE EATEN...
DARREN SHAN
NUMBER ONE MASTER OF HORROR
Dark Calling
CAN YOU HEAR THE VOICES...?